They stared at [...] *for several wordless moments, the atmosphere between them heavy as a drug.*

'Carl . . .' she whispered at last in husky accents, but he appeared not to have heard. She might have been looking at the face of a man who had suffered the agonies of hell itself and emerged covered with scars. She shivered and the surging wave of fear that swept through her body was more than mental.

'So, I have the pleasure of meeting you again, Sarah.' His grip was a vise that made her flinch. 'You haven't changed much,' he added, the piercing black eyes roving her figure, insulting in their examination of her body, stripping it naked. Her heart raced. She had seen the dark fanatical look of desire in a man's eyes before . . . but this . . . She tried to turn from him, but his very personality held her, every shred of composure stolen by the compulsion of those piercing black eyes.

ANNE HAMPSON

has the same impetuous streak as her heroines. It often lands her in the middle of a new country, a new adventure—and a new book. Her first-hand knowledge of her settings and her lively characters have combined to delight her readers throughout the world.

Dear Reader:

Silhouette Romances is an exciting new publishing venture. We will be presenting the very finest writers of contemporary romantic fiction as well as outstanding new talent in this field. It is our hope that our stories, our heroes and our heroines will give you, the reader, all you want from romantic fiction.

Also, *you* play an important part in our future plans for Silhouette Romances. We welcome any suggestions or comments on our books and I invite you to write to us at the address below.

So, enjoy this book and all the wonderful romances from Silhouette. They're for *you!*

Karen Solem
Editor-in-Chief
Silhouette Books
P. O. Box 769
New York, N.Y. 10019

ANNE HAMPSON
Payment in Full

Silhouette Romance

Published by Silhouette Books New York

America's Publisher of Contemporary Romance

Other Silhouette Romances by Anne Hampson

Payment in Full
Stormy Masquerade
Second Tomorrow
The Dawn Steals Softly
Man of the Outback
Where Eagles Nest

Man Without a Heart
Enchantment
Fascination
Desire
Realm of the Pagans

SILHOUETTE BOOKS, a Simon & Schuster Division of
GULF & WESTERN CORPORATION
1230 Avenue of the Americas, New York, N.Y. 10020

ISBN: 0-671-57001-3

First Silhouette printing May, 1980

10 9 8 7 6 5

Chapter One

Why she should be thinking of one man while another was proposing marriage to her Sarah could not say. But through the reality of the present there drifted the face and figure of a tall lithe Greek, a man from the mists of memory who, with the passing of the years, had until now gradually become a nebulous shadow, unreal.

'Does it need so much consideration, Sarah?' Eric Vernon's quiet voice brought her blue eyes back to his face, and the dark classical features of Carl Duris were blotted out, but only fleetingly.

'Are you serious?' she asked, not because she was playing for time, but because the pull of her mind was beckoning her thoughts back to Carl. A handsome face, unscarred as yet by the hurts that life could inflict; its only lines were those of laughter. Yet, in repose the separate features were more than a little formidable, the deep-set eyes as black as pitchblende, the thrusting jaw spelling mastery and arrogance, the full-lipped mouth sensuous and yet arrogantly firm. His hair, she recalled, was gleaming black with a

persistent wave which he seemed to resent, so that he
made a determined effort to brush it away from his
forehead. She liked the wave, she had said; therefore,
he must leave it alone. In the gentle, good-humoured
way he adopted towards her, Carl had pandered to her
wish, for the very simple reason that he was madly in
love with her.

Why had she refused him her disbelieving employer
had asked, for surely she was willing to own that he
was the most eligible man she had ever met, or was
ever likely to meet. Why? Because she had no
intention of putting her head in a noose in the way her
mother had done, enduring years of misery with a
man who was faithless, extravagant and even cruel.
Then Avril, her sister, disillusioned after only a year
and a half and only now beginning to recover from the
heartache of losing her husband to another woman.
Not for Sarah a mistake of that kind; she was content
to remain single, to be her own mistress, answerable
to no one. She turned down the Greek's offer and a
smile touched her lips even now as she dwelt on his
reaction.

'You want to remain single!' The accent was more
pronounced than usual but to Sarah's ears it was just
as attractive as ever. She liked his foreign voice, just
as she liked everything else about him, for in addition
to the superlative qualities of his face and form he was
kind and gentle and compassionate. All any woman
could wish for, if that woman happened to be brave
enough to take a chance on marriage.

'I don't believe that any girl of eighteen could
possibly want to stay single. In my country all girls
want to marry and have babies—'

'I'm not from your country, Carl,' she broke in to
remind him. 'But that has nothing to do with it. The

experiences of my mother and sister are more than enough to turn me against marriage. If I can learn by the experiences of others, why should I be foolhardy enough to risk learning by my own?'

Fury had looked out of eyes that had hitherto regarded her with great tenderness and love.

'That's a strange logic,' he rasped. 'In fact, it isn't logic at all!'

'It happens to be my kind of logic, Carl. Please take no for an answer; you're only fighting a losing battle.'

He had been forced to accept her decision; she knew he was heartbroken, but he was a Greek and would soon recover. He would marry, because Greeks were known to be the most amorous men in the world. By what process of assessment this had been proved she could not possibly guess, but she did know that if Carl was an example then certainly Greek men knew how to love.

'I want you, Sarah,' he had whispered in her ear on one occasion when in blissful ignorance she had allowed him to take her into the gardens below the Acropolis of Athens at dead of night. They were returning to her hotel from a dinner-dance and instead of calling a taxi he had suggested they walk. He knew a shortcut to the hotel. . . . 'You're my ideal. You'll make the most exciting lover. . . .' She had expected him to kiss her, and as she wanted him to, it was in a state of pleasant expectancy that she stood in the circle of his arm, her sweet young face lifted, her eyes aglow in the light from a full moon which created a fairyland around the sacred buildings high above them—the temples of Zeus and Athena standing out in splendid majesty on the Acropolis. His mouth came down, gentle, as she had known it would be, and in the sudden eagerness that came to her unbidden, she reciprocated in a way that set his pagan instincts on fire. Without warning she was swept into the vortex of primitive, nerve-firing passion, her protesting body crushed against his virility as his loins melded with hers. Her lips parted at the moist insistence and mastery of his sensuous mouth, and with a stifled little gasp of disbelief she felt his tongue enter and probe. Instinctively she began to use her own tongue to expel it, an action that proved to be her own undoing, for the contact and movement of her tongue against his only served to add fuel to the flame of his passion and for a long moment she was the victim of her own awakened desires, drawn irrevocably into a conflagration of pagan love-making against which any resistance on her part could not a possibly survive. He slid his hand beneath her evening blouse, and as, after unclipping her bra, he took one firm small breast into his hand, she truly believed her virginity must be nearing its end. For as he caressed the nipple, raising it to the hardness of sense-shattering desire, spasm after spasm of sheer undiluted ecstasy throbbed with violent intensity through her whole body. 'Remain single,' he was to say later, in very different circumstances after she had refused his offer of marriage. 'You're made for love, Sarah, and I've proved it to you— No, don't blush. It was natural and beautiful—it could have been more beautiful if we had lain together in the gardens, beneath the moon, and made real love. Let me show you,' he pleaded. 'When we're married I'll make love to you in romantic places . . . beneath the palms on the beach of my island, or maybe in the warm water when we've been swimming in the sea— There are places where the rocks can shelter us, but it's our own private beach anyway. You will like my island, Sarah,' he had continued with a sort of desperate urgency in his attractive foreign voice. 'It's a gentle place, quiet and far from the bustle of cities like Athens. The people are friendly and kind, but poor. They don't trouble about their poverty, though—' he smiled, his black eyes far away—'because they have sunshine and flowers and beautiful scenery. . . .' Although twenty-six years of age, he had seemed like a boy, uninhibited, a dreamer with pure, idealistic visions; he saw a future with Sarah as nothing but roses and red wine. . . .

No wonder he had seemed to hate her in the end, when he was forced to accept her decision.

She had been with her present employer—Eric Vernon, president of a firm which went by the name of Villas Abroad—for about six months when she met the handsome Carl Duris at a business conference held at an hotel in Athens. Eric had been invited, and as his secretary she had naturally accompanied him.

Carl's only relative, his great-uncle, a millionaire citrus-fruit grower, had been at the conference, and Carl, as his heir, had been with him. And from the moment he set eyes on Sarah Carl had known that at last he had met the one girl in the world whom he desired for his wife. For a whole fortnight he had worked desperately to get what he wanted, taking her out, giving her a wonderful time, but it proved in the end to be in vain, and he had gone away a broken man.

A small, impatient cough from her employer brought Sarah back with a start to the present, and to the question she had just asked him. Her blue eyes lifted inquiringly, a trifle puzzled.

'I asked if you were serious,' she reminded him.

'And I answered you,' he returned curtly. 'You were miles away and didn't hear me. Yes, of course I'm serious. Will you marry me?'

She could have laughed, knowing as she did what a womaniser he was. Until recently she had often acted as a buffer between him and some infatuated female who, after he had taken what he wanted and then thrown her over, would persist in attempting to bring the romance to life again, telephoning or writing letters, and some even went as far as to call in at the office and demand to see their fickle lover.

'You know my sentiments on marriage, Eric,' she replied, lifting a shapely hand to flick a wisp of golden hair from her face. 'In any case,' she added, 'you're the last man I'd think of marrying. The risk would be enormous.'

He frowned darkly at her and said, 'The wild oats are sown, Sarah. I want to settle down to a home routine—have three or four children. I know you like kids, too, because I've seen you with your little godchild—'

'Eric,' she broke in softly, 'it isn't any use. I'm a confirmed bachelor girl. I advise you to look elsewhere for the mother of those children you mentioned. I admit I like children and would love to have a family of my own—but in no way would I tread the road of marriage just to pick them up as I went along.'

He frowned again. 'Don't be crude, Sarah!'

She had to laugh. 'That'—with a lift of her delicately curving brows—'from you?'

He had the grace to look away, and she studied him in profile—the clear-cut lines, pleasing but not strong, the large sensuous mouth that sometimes made her wonder how many women had been tempted by it, the light brown hair, wavy and thick. An attractive man, undoubtedly, but insipid in comparison to Carl. . . . Her forehead puckered. Why should he intrude into her consciousness like this? She supposed it was because of Eric's proposal of marriage; it was bringing back the memory of the other man in her life who had proposed marriage.

'Are you turning me down?' Eric spoke into the quiet, a sigh in his voice, as if he had already accepted defeat.

'Eric, you know I am.' It was Sarah's turn to sigh. Her job as secretary was just about as enjoyable as any job could be, and she hoped it would be hers for many years to come—until she retired at the age of sixty, perhaps. But in any case, at least until Eric decided to retire. 'We're good friends, let's keep it that way.'

His eyes flickered over her, faintly resentful as they took in the fine moulding of her features, the flawless, peach-bloom quality of her skin. Her lips—which he had once said were made to be kissed—tilted attractively at the corners, appearing in some mysterious way to enhance even further the small, retroussé nose with its delicately arched nostrils. Her hair, a glorious halo for the beauty it framed, was like finely spun gold sprinkled with starlight. He had always been vitally aware of her beauty but, wise businessman that he was, he had decided from the start to play it safe. Secretaries of her calibre were almost impossible to get; he had no intention of losing her. And he knew without any doubt at all that, with the first unguarded move on his part, he would be looking for another secretary.

'I want you for my wife as well as my friend, Sarah.' He was trying hard while at the same time realising the futility of his efforts. 'You'll still be my secretary—'

'With four children?' she interrupted, eyebrows raised again. 'Are you suggesting I go native and have an hour or so off to have my babies? And what about afterwards?'

'A nanny. People in our station don't look after their own children. A nanny at first, and then boarding-school. That's how it goes with those of us who can afford the expense.'

'Do you know, Eric,' she mused, 'apart from any-thing else, you and I are on entirely different wave-lengths regarding marriage and the raising of a family. You see, most parents want the pleasure of their children, especially today when the childhood years are so short—most children being little adults by the time they're nine or ten.'

'Oh, well, let's not talk about it,' he decided at last. 'I expect someone else will turn up to fit the bill.'

'Don't you want to fall in love?' she asked him interestedly.

'Like you, I don't think much of it. However, unlike you I believe that a marriage between you and me could succeed. We've a great deal in common, no matter what you think to the contrary.' He leant back in his chair after taking a glass from the table. He and Sarah were having dinner at the Medway, an hotel set back from the bank of the river in Kent from which it had taken its name. Eric had been visiting a prospec-tive client who was considering buying one of his luxury villas on the island of Abaco in the Bahamas. He had been undecided and in the end Eric told him to think it over, and they left. It was well after eight o'clock by that time, and Eric suggested they have dinner at the first suitable restaurant they came to.

Eric asked for a table by the window, where they could have a good view of the river and the small pleasure-boats sailing along its placid waters. From one small cruiser a dog jumped overboard, took a cooling swim and then ran along the bank, keeping pace with the boat until the owner slowed down to enable him to leap aboard again.

'They're having fun,' remarked Eric, and some strange quality in his voice arrested her attention. 'It's all right for some.' Regarding his secretary from above the rim of his wine glass, he put it to his lips and sipped the clear amber liquid. 'I wish you'd given me a different answer,' he said unexpectedly.

'Don't keep on,' she begged. 'Life's very pleasant as it is.'

'You have these notions about not getting married, but . . .' He stopped as if putting a deliberate brake on his tongue, yet seconds later it seemed he could not hold back the words, '. . . you were married once, remember?'

She closed her eyes, a glacier chill freezing the blood in her veins.

'How can you remind me of it?' she cried. 'It's past and gone—dead as the man I married.' Another shudder made it necessary to put down the glass she had only just taken from the table.

'Sorry, Sarah. I don't know why I brought it up.' His voice was apologetic but the expression in his eyes was almost one of envy. 'Married for ten minutes . . . a fortune the reward. . . . Not bad!'

'Please, Eric, I'm not talking about it.'

'Sorry,' he said again, and the subject was closed.

Eric dropped Sarah at the door of her London flat, but instead of going to bed she made herself a beaker of tea and took it into the sitting-room, where, after opening the door-type window, she stepped through it

onto a small balcony just large enough to accommo-
date two garden chairs and a wrought-iron table. She
sat down with the tea, her brooding eyes sweeping the
dark shapes of the trees in Hyde Park. Why was she
feeling different tonight? For several years she had
glided along the smooth path of her life, looking
neither forward nor backward, content with today.
She had a comfortable flat, a small car, an enviable
post with a high salary and numerous perks.

In all the seven years she had worked for Eric
Vernon, there had been only one dark blot—other than
the death of her mother five years ago.

It had begun about a month after she had turned
down Carl's offer of marriage, when, back in England,
content to devote all her energies to her job, she had
gone home one evening to find her mother in tears,
and her father standing with his back to the empty
fireplace, a scowl on his face.

'What's wrong?' Sarah at eighteen took everything
to heart, especially her mother's unhappiness. She
had suffered untold misery at the hands of her
husband, and Sarah failed completely to understand
how she could still be in love with him, but she
was—as madly in love as on the day she had married
him, it would appear.

'It's me again,' her father cut in, gritting his teeth.
'I'm always doing something I shouldn't!'

Sarah's eyes flashed with indignation at his attitude
of near-martyrdom. It was always the same; he would
do something drastically wrong, then when his wife
complained, he adopted this air of injured innocence,
which was galling enough to Sarah, so she hated to
think what it did to her mother, the chief sufferer for
many years past.

'What have you done?' asked Sarah, her spirits low

because there would be a week at least of dissension, there always was. 'Another woman?'

'Not this time,' chokingly from her mother. 'He's robbed his employer of eight thousand pounds!'

Frozen to immobility by the chill that swept along her spine, Sarah could only gape; even her lips were too stiff for movement.

'I gambled it all away,' offered her father, like a small boy wanting to get it all over and done with. 'And I'm threatened with jail if I don't pay it back in a week.'

'A week. . . .' Sarah managed to speak at last. 'How . . . how c-can you p-pay it back?'

'He can't, so he'll go to prison!' The last word was a shriek of despair and to Sarah's horror her mother slumped in the chair and would have fallen sideways onto the floor if she had not sped across the room to catch her in her strong young arms. Her father just stood there, immune to his wife's suffering, as he had always been immune to it. Both Sarah and her sister had many times begged their mother to leave him, but always in vain. Her love for the rogue she had married was too strong. She'd rather die than leave him, she had told her girls, and she meant it.

'She needs the doctor,' faltered Sarah, her heart leaping in her breast as she saw the deep purple colour that had come to her mother's lips. 'Father . . . I'm . . . I'm frightened,' she whispered, easing the inert figure back onto the chair. 'Can't you help me!' she cried when he remained unmoving. 'God, are you so heartless that you can stand there, just staring vacantly when Mother's ill!'

But her mother opened her eyes at that moment, reviving sufficiently to refuse to have the doctor.

Sarah had gone the following day to see the tall

gaunt business tycoon who was her father's employer. And the moment she set eyes on him some uncanny instinct warned her of an approaching, inescapable doom. He desired her on sight, in a very different way from that in which the gentle Carl had desired her. It was a carnal, lascivious desire, a lustful craving for her lovely virgin body.

'I'll take you in exchange,' he had said with a leer. 'I'm offering you marriage, though, so think yourself highly honoured!'

Shocked to the very depths, Sarah had made a hasty departure, only to arrive home to find her mother prone on the couch, and her father nowhere to be seen. With frantic haste Sarah phoned the doctor.

Half an hour later she was hearing him say, 'A heart attack. She'll get over it this time but she'll have to take everything very slowly from now on. The next attack could be the last.'

'You m-mean . . . mean . . . she'll die? . . .'

The doctor nodded his head.

'Make sure that she's always kept quiet. A shock, however small, or any kind of upset, could mean death for her.'

The trees in the park began to sway as a breeze came up from the east. Sarah shivered, picked up the beaker, and went inside, closing the window and and pulling the cord which closed the drapes. Her mental narrative had reached the final chapter, for although she had married Arthur Grimsby, he had never realised his ambition to own her. Having been drinking for several hours prior to the wedding ceremony at the Registrar's Office, he had staggered out, smugly satisfied with his day's work, and, omitting the courtesy of opening the near-side door for his bride, he had swung into the road with the intention of getting into the driver's seat of his Rolls. . . .

The verdict was accidental death with no blame attached to the driver of the passing lorry, who had done his best to avoid the accident. The press scooped up the story of the well-known tycoon's untimely death only minutes after his fashionable wedding. His tragic, broken-hearted bride was in no fit condition to be interviewed. . . .

There had been no existing will and so Sarah had come into a fortune, but knowing that her father would not rest until he had managed to get some of it from her, with the result that her mother would suffer more acutely than ever, she felt justified in telling a lie. So Sarah told her mother and father that she had been left nothing. Only two people knew she had inherited the fortune: her employer and her sister. Recently she had asked her solicitor to investigate various charities and on his recommendation she intended to give the whole vast sum away.

Chapter Two

The following day being Saturday, Sarah was in no hurry to get her breakfast. She made a cup of tea and took it back to bed, sitting up against the pillows while she listened to the news on the radio. But her thoughts repeatedly brought back the events of last night. Why had Eric proposed marriage when he could be sure he had no possible chance of being accepted? It was not only on account of her attitude towards marriage; it was also that, with her knowledge of his philandering ways, she would be mad to have accepted him. And why had he brought up the one subject which he knew would upset her? He had mentioned the fortune, speaking as if she had benefited by it, when he knew full well that she intended giving it away. His whole manner had been puzzling, now she came to think of it. Having worked for him for seven years, she had believed she knew his every mood, but last night there was something unfathomable about him which disturbed her, made her feel uneasy. She had already suspected that his dissolute life was beginning to pall because about six months ago his life-style had changed. Not only had he made fewer dates with his various girl-friends, but, strangely, he had begun cutting down on his expenses all round. He had dismissed the couple who took care of him at his country house which backed on to a small cove in Dorset, and even at his flat in Park Lane daily help had been substituted for the housekeeper he had had for several years.

Cuts had also been made in his business expenses, clients being taken to a small hotel for lunch when it used to be the Ritz.

Telling herself it was none of her business, Sarah rose at length, and after taking a bath and washing her hair, she tackled the domestic chores that were reserved for the week-end. She was expecting her sister for dinner, and as Avril rarely honoured her with a visit she was happily looking forward to seeing her. She had planned a rather special meal, for which the pleasant task of preparation took up most of the afternoon, but as Sarah was always well-organised, she had ample time left both for the flower arrange-

ments for the dinner table and for her appearance. So
when her sister arrived she was looking fresh and cool
in an ankle-length leisure gown of printed cotton. Her
hair shone with its usual golden lustre; her eyes were
bright, her smile spontaneous.

Avril, swift with the flattering remark that she
looked younger every time she saw her, added with a
tinge of envy, 'How do you do it?' At which Sarah
merely shrugged and Avril said warningly. 'Wait till
you're turned thirty; it's then that the trouble starts.'

'In what way?' Sarah was pouring a dry sherry for
Avril and a martini for herself. 'I'm not expecting any
grey hairs until I'm sixty.'

'What an optimist you are! I wish I had your
personality!'

'There's nothing wrong with yours,' Sarah assured
her, transferring the drinks to a small occasional table
she had previously brought forward. 'I'll be with you
in a moment. I want to look at the steak.'

Avril was deep in thought when she returned.

'How's your job?' Sarah asked. 'You were rather
unsettled the last time we met.'

'I still am. . . .' She slid her sister a glance from
under her lashes. 'I talked to you about a boutique I
wanted to buy, remember?'

Sarah nodded. 'It wasn't for sale, though.'

'The owner hadn't made up her mind, but she did
tell me I could have the first refusal. Well, she's
selling. It's a dream, Sarah, very distinctive clothes.
She has all the best agencies, mainly French.'

'It sounds just right for you. It'll be better than
working for someone else for the rest of your days.'
Sarah sat down opposite to her, deciding that Avril
was letting herself go instead of keeping young. Her
skin was flawless but too pale, her hair clean but dull,

as if she had used the wrong shampoo. The dress she wore was creased from being against others in her wardrobe; five minutes with a hot iron would have made all the difference to it. Sarah tried to imagine her as proprietor of a fashionable boutique and wondered if she would automatically smarten herself up, as an apt advertisement for her fashionable merchandise.

'But *you* obviously intend working for someone else for the rest of your days?'

'I'm happy in my job.' Sarah picked up her glass, moving it to hear the ice tinkle on the side. 'I've no money for going into business on my own even if I wanted to. It costs a great deal these days.'

Silence. Avril leant forward to take up her glass. 'You have a fortune,' she reminded her sister quietly at last.

'It's not mine, I'm giving it away—'

'What? Are you crazy!'

'I don't want it.' Sarah sipped her drink, a frown on her brow. Each time Avril visited her she brought up the question of the money. 'As far as I'm concerned, it's tainted.' Her lovely face was set, her eyes darker than normal. 'In any case, that beast would never have left it to me if he'd had time to make a will!'

'Tainted or not, I wish it were mine. You're not serious about giving it away, surely?'

'I was never more serious. I should have done it long ago.'

'I want that boutique,' murmured Avril after a small hesitation, 'and I haven't the money for it.'

Sarah's eyes were perceptive. 'You want me to lend you some money?'

'If you're set on giving it away—then why don't you begin with me? After all, it's said that charity begins at home.' Avril gave a long deep sigh as if to say, 'There, it's out. I had difficulty in coming to the point but I managed it.'

'I'll give you some,' agreed Sarah. 'How much do you want?'

'About forty thousand pounds. The stock's been runing low recently and I shall have to replenish it. The whole place wants decorating too, and new carpets, and models.'

'All right. Forty thousand. I'll have it transferred to your bank if you give me your account number.'

After her sister had left Sarah sat thoughtfully on the couch. It was plain as to the reason for Avril's visit, but although Sarah was hurt by the knowledge that had come to her, she was at the same time aware of her sister's envy, and as Avril had said, if she intended getting rid of the money, why not let charity begin at home?

The following Monday morning Sarah was called into Eric's office, and to her astonishment and disbelief he asked her again if she would marry him.

'What's the matter with you?' she demanded, shaking her head impatiently. 'Can't you take no for an answer?'

He set his mouth and she had the sudden conviction that he was far more angered than hurt by her refusal.

'Don't you ever get lonely?'

'Not so lonely that I'd risk marriage.'

'Risk!' he gritted. 'You've a damned obsession about marriage, Sarah. Don't you think you're going a bit far?'

Her chin had lifted as he mentioned an obsession, but now she was more puzzled than indignant.

'Why the urgency, Eric?' she asked in a very quiet voice. 'I'm beginning to think that there's something I don't understand.'

He bit his lip and turned away, hiding his expression.

'There's no urgency,' he denied. 'I've recently begun to think I ought to marry—'

'But you don't love me,' she interrupted. 'People usually fall in love before they decide to marry.'

The phone rang and he picked up the receiver. Watching his face, Sarah saw his expression change from interest to alarm in a matter of seconds. Little grey lines were creeping up the sides of his mouth, like veins beneath the skin slowly draining of blood. Tiny beads of perspiration gathered on his forehead, glistening in the harsh light from the desk lamp, which was always on no matter what the time of day.

'Yes . . . yes, I'm fully aware . . .' His breath seemed to become difficult, and he paused, listening. 'But that's impossible!' he exclaimed in a strangled voice. 'I just can't meet a. . . .' His words slurred to silence as he suddenly realised that his secretary was sitting there. An imperious flick of the hand sent her away, cheeks burning. Never in all the years she had worked for him had he done a thing like that. Something was wrong . . . gravely wrong.

Later that day he called her into his office, this time to inform her that they would be going to Greece in five days' time.

'Greece? You're buying some more property there?'

He nodded. He seemed to have aged ten years in the last four or five hours.

'By a strange coincidence the villa's offered to me by your old flame, Carl Duris.'

She gave a start. 'That certainly is a coincidence.'
She frowned. 'He's offered you a house?'

'That's right. It's on the island of Comaris, where he
lives.'

'Is that in the Aegean?' She spoke mechanically,
her mind not on the location of the island but on the
man who lived there. What differences would she see
in him after almost seven years? He was sure to be
married, and there would be children, for all Greeks
want children, sons, not daughters, usually. But Carl,
being wealthy, might not mind a daughter or two; it
was only the peasants who prayed to the saints not to
send them daughters, for daughters had to be provided with dowries—*prika,* as it was called in Greece.

'Yes, it's in the Aegean. We'll have to fly to Rhodes
and from there we'll go by Carl's private launch.
There's no airfield on Comaris. Carl won't have one.'

Her eyes flickered with interest. 'It's his own private
property?'

'It would seem so.'

'You've been in touch with him? I haven't opened
any letters—'

'He phoned me—one day last week, at my home. I
feel we can make a lot of money if we hold on to the
villa for a year and then sell it.'

'It seems very strange that he's offering property for
sale.' Sarah's nerves were taut. So many things
seemed to be happening all at once—first there was
Eric's totally unexpected offer of marriage, then his
reference to the money she had inherited, which he
had never mentioned at any time in the past. And now
there was this house for sale, which necessitated their
going to the island owned by Carl Duris. 'I shouldn't
have thought he'd need to sell a house,' she went on

when Eric did not speak. 'His great-uncle was a millionaire and Carl was his sole heir.'

Eric shrugged. His interest was in the property, not the private affairs of the man who was selling it.

'Most people sell a house sometime,' he said.

'Is it his own house, then? Is he going to live somewhere else?' She was still exceedingly puzzled. 'If he wants to sell, why can't he sell to someone closer at hand?'

'Probably because he can't find a buyer. If it's a small island, then obviously there's a paucity of potential customers. In any case,' he pointed out, 'our business depends on buying property abroad.'

'But why pick on you?' she persisted. 'It's all very odd, Eric, you have to admit that.'

'It's a little puzzling,' he agreed, but went on to remind her that their advertisements were inserted periodically in most of the newspapers in Europe and the Middle East. 'He's probably seen one of those ads, and, having met me before, thought he'd give me the business.'

'Did he talk about me?' she queried after a pause.

'He asked me if you were still with me, and I said yes.' He glanced curiously at her. 'It was strange, but I had the impression that he knew you were still with me.'

'You did?' Nerves tingled, and her heart began beating rather too quickly for comfort. 'How could he?' she asked.

'I haven't a clue. He does a great deal of trade with this country, remember. He might come over now and then, on business . . .' He broke off with a gesture of impatience, and no more was said on the subject until Sarah, ready to arrange the flight, asked if it was really necessary for her to go with him.

'Of course it is.' He looked astounded by the question. 'You're my secretary, so you must come with me. Besides, I detest travelling alone, you know that.'

The cabin cruiser which they boarded in the harbour of Mandraki on Rhodes was the last word in luxury, but with the meeting with Carl uppermost in her mind, Sarah made no attempt to explore. She merely sat in the saloon, a tangle of undisciplined thoughts circling around in her brain. For the past few days she had been profoundly conscious of a mental disturbance which she could neither describe nor analyse. This trip was, in the main, like any other: Eric was going to view property with the possibility of buying it for resale later. The only difference should have been the minor one of their both having met the vendor some years previously, and perhaps the slightly more important factor of the vendor having proposed marriage to Sarah. But looming large in her mind was the conviction that something far more momentous than all this was to be the outcome of the trip. When she woke this morning an almost physical feeling of doom seemed to be enveloping her, and she had actually toyed with the idea of telling Eric she was off-colour and asking to be excused.

'It's a super craft, isn't it?' Eric came to her after having asked one of the two crew members if he could take a look all over the boat. 'Carl uses it merely for transport, the bloke out there was telling me. Apparently none of the ferries from Piraeus or from Rhodes call at his island. He won't have them.' Sarah said nothing, and he stood regarding her in silence for some moments before commenting on her appearance. 'You look especially charming today, Sarah. That outfit suits you.'

She merely nodded her head. He had assured her that his business with Carl would take only two days at the most, so apart from the leaf-green linen suit she had travelled in, she had brought only two cotton dresses and one evening dress. Her accessories to the suit were white suede—belt, handbag and sandals—all of which had been with it when she saw the suit on a model in one of London's most exclusive shops. She had seen at once that it was just right for her, and in spite of the price—which seemed exorbitant for what it was—Sarah had decided to buy it.

'We're getting near to the island,' Eric was saying sometime later when he came to her again. 'Come outside and take a look. Petros had been showing me a map, so I can pick out Comaris for you from the several other islands in its vicinity.'

She went with him, feeling cold and wondering why. For although the sun was beginning to fall, its rays were still warm.

After pointing out the island to her, Eric went off to talk to Petros, who was steering the boat. Sarah stood by the rail, her brooding gaze fixed upon the island of Comaris, which seemed, from this distance, to be rather more rocky than its neighbours, some of which appeared to be uninhabited.

As the launch drew nearer she saw that her first impression was correct and that Comaris was some-what rocky, especially in the north, with cliffs, magnificent and precarious, dropping sheer down to the sea. Approaching as they were from the west, and with the island narrowing almost to a point at this end, it was possible to see its southern side as well. Here was a gentler aspect, whose softer lower slopes were clothed with lush green vegetation which swept down in nature's glorious abandon to where the waves broke like filmy white lace onto the shore. So peaceful it all looked!—with, nestling on the hillsides, a flat-roofed cubic house here and there, and sometimes two or three together. In one small community cradled by the hills a church could be discerned, its gleaming white campanile silhouetted against the sky.

'Ah, there you are.' Eric came and stood by her side. 'I thought you'd gone back to the saloon.' He looked at her. 'You're pale,' he observed. 'Anything wrong?'

'I shall be glad when it's all over,' she returned. 'I wish I hadn't come with you.'

'Carl?' He seemed indifferent to her troubled expression. 'I don't know what you're worrying about. He can't eat you.'

'He was very angry when we parted,' she murmured reminiscently.

'I dare say he was. Greeks are used to getting their own way. In his country marriages are often arranged, even in these enlightened times, and so if he'd been there and set his fancy on a girl, he'd only have to offer for her and he'd get her. She wouldn't have any say in the matter if her father accepted an offer on her behalf.'

Sarah was frowning darkly. 'It's an unbelievable custom!' she exclaimed angrily. 'Why don't the girls rise up and fight for their rights?'

'One day they will. In the big cities girls are more free, more influenced by the West, but in the villages the old customs die hard; but you know as much about it as I do,' he ended, turning his attention to the island on which they would be setting foot in a quarter of an hour or so.

'Will there be a car to meet us?' Sarah's own attention was on the island, and as her eyes picked out the houses more clearly, she saw that the gardens surrounding them were dripping with exotic colour from hibiscus and oleander, from roses and passion flowers and trailing bougainvillaea vines rioting in glorious profusion over trellises and low stone walls.

'Yes, there'll be a car.'

The sun was already going down, its slanting rays piercing thin cirrus clouds to soften the mountain crags and thread their golden strands into the foothills on the southern side of the island. Uncertainty, anxiety and a strange nameless fear all mingled within Sarah's mind, rendering it impossible for her to think intelligently about the forthcoming meeting with the man whose wife she could have been.

The launch drew alongside the jetty; they stepped from it into the waiting car and were driven by a dark, stocky Greek whose ready welcoming smile revealed several gold fillings interspersed by gaps in his teeth.

'You haf good journey from England, yes?'

'Very good,' replied Eric affably.

The driver took a sweep off the waterfront, steering the car into a winding, tree-lined road leading into the hills, and there on a lush green plateau was the modern villa, its southern wing raised on stilts so that the rooms commanded a panoramic view of the whole circle of the bay and across the smooth cerulean waters to the other small islands and, in the distance, to Rhodes itself.

Sarah gasped as the car came to a crunching halt on the gravel of a semi-circular forecourt and the Greek driver, whose name was Takis, opened the door for her.

'My master is waiting for you.' He smiled, but for the moment Sarah had no inclination to move. She wanted to stare and stare, her senses alive to the incredible view, and the scene of breathtaking beauty surrounding her on all sides—the majestic mountain peaks rising like sentinels against a sky of sunset gold, the sea of aged olive trees occupying what appeared to be a raised beach of ancient origin and, between them and the tree-line, the natural vegetation of the island—cypresses and pines, the glossy carob trees and tall, stately palms.

She turned, her spellbound senses taking in the continuous flow of colour and perfume and the hum of insects in the flowers, wisteria cloaking a high wall, magenta and crimson bougainvillaea tumbling in glorious disarray over the long pergola bordering a terrace, and parterres and flower-beds intruding into the ordered smoothness of well-manicured lawns, flaunting colour with their roses and canna lilies, passion flowers and numberless other exotic delights. A clear blue swimming-pool was visible through a gap in a hedge of hibiscus bushes, and on its patio white chairs with gaily coloured cretonne covers could be seen. Flowers in attractive clay urns decorated the patio. Finally she brought her eyes to the house itself. Built of white stone, with large windows, blue shut-tered outside but with the suggestion of hand-embroidered net inside, it was sheer perfection both in form and in the site it occupied.

A strange feeling encompassed her, a mingling of yearning and uncertainty. The meeting with Carl was almost upon her, affecting her now to the exclusion of all else. She looked at Eric, turned and followed the man who was leading the way up a flight of white stone steps flanked by fluted columns of gleaming white marble.

In response to the clang of a heavy brass knocker, the door was opened by a servant who spoke with a

slight accent, inviting them in and saying brightly,
'Mr Vernon and Miss Holmes. My master is expecting
you.'

Again Sarah stared, awed by the tasteful splendour
of the entrance hall with its beautiful antique furniture, its dramatically placed climbing plants that
wound round and up two white stone columns to
cover the arch above them; and its impressive balus-
traded staircase. 'This way, please.' The manservant
was urging them to follow him, and a moment later he
had opened the door of a large elegantly furnished
lounge and was saying, 'Mr Carlos—the lady and
gentleman.'

Dressed from head to foot in black, the sole occu-
pant of the room had been standing with his back to
them, looking through a window, and it immediately
struck Sarah that he must have known they were here
but that he was having them formally announced by
the manservant, who appeared to fill the role of butler.
He turned slowly, his arrogant shoulders straight and
square. Ignoring Eric, he gave his full attention to
Sarah, whose eyes, widening to their fullest extent,
betrayed the incredulity of her mind. This, it was
saying, couldn't possibly be the laughing carefree Carl
Duris whom I once knew!

She and he stared at one another for several
wordless moments, the atmosphere between them
heavy as a drug.

'Carl. . . .' she whispered at last in husky accents,
but he appeared not to have heard. She might have
been looking at the face of a man who had suffered
the agonies of hell itself and emerged covered with
scars. Every feature had changed: the mouth was
sensuous still, but thinned by lines of ruthlessness

and even cruelty; the nostrils were wide, flaring; the eyes, dark as the pitchblende to which she had previously likened them, were black pools of hate. Deeply ingrained lines ran down each side of his mouth and across his forehead. It was the face of a pagan, primitively ruthless and cruel. She shivered, and the surging wave of fear that swept through her body was more than mental. A pallor stole into her cheeks, and the palms of her hands felt damp.

'So I have the pleasure of meeting you again, Sarah.' The voice had changed; Sarah shivered again at the guttural quality of its tone. His hand came out; she wished she could have ignored it, but she dared not. His grip was a vise that made her flinch. 'You haven't changed much,' he added, the piercing black eyes roving her figure, insulting in their examination of her body, stripping it naked. Her heart raced. She had seen the dark fanatic look of desire in a man's eyes before . . . but this . . . She tried to turn from him, but his very personality held her, every shred of composure stolen by the compulsion of those piercing black eyes.

But at last she was released from the mesmerising stare and a great shuddering sigh rose like a sob from the very depths of her being. She was limp in body and weak of limb. Seeking the support of a chair, she sank into it without being asked.

She saw him turn to look Eric over, and again Sarah found herself staring in disbelief, this time because of the instant and dramatic change in his manner as he prepared to speak to her employer. There was a dignified, arrogant, superior air about him, an air of distinction which made Eric appear less than ordinary in comparison. Carl's attitude dominated the room with the iron sway of his dynamic personality, and even Eric seemed to cower. The man was unhuman! Sarah saw him as a Greek god of pagan times, exerting his celestial power without any conscious knowledge of it.

'So you're interested in buying property in the Greek islands, Mr. Vernon?' Sauve, the tone; impersonal as the look in his eyes. 'We shall take dinner early, and after that you and I shall talk business.'

Eric inclined his head, politely thanked Carl for the offer of dinner, and agreed to his suggestion about talking business afterwards.

Five minutes later Sarah was sitting on the bed in the room to which she had been shown by a trim maid in black whose name was Androula.

That some terrible calamity had overtaken Carl, Sarah could not doubt, for everything about him was changed and he seemed to have drifted back through the centuries to the days of his pagan ancestors— Sarah cut her thoughts, realising that she was allowing them to run away with her. Yet a moment later she had risen from the bed and was restlessly pacing the bedroom floor, telling herself sternly that this mind-tension must stop. She ought not to let herself be so deeply affected by the change in Carl. In less than forty-eight hours she would leave this island, never to cross paths with him again.

She went to the window and stared out to the darkening sea, trying desperately to put him out of her mind. But it was impossible. She wanted to know what had caused the change, what had robbed him of those wonderful traits of gentleness and compassion, what had stripped him of his ideals. . . . Was it some terrible tragedy—or perhaps an illness that had brought him, in fearful agony, to death's door? She could not accept this latter, simply because that sort of experience would never have brought about such a dramatic change in his character. She tried to find other explanations but failed, and she did wonder if she would be any wiser when, Eric having conducted his business deal to his satisfaction, they would leave Comaris for ever. She went at last to the bathroom and showered. Then she took out the long dress from her suitcase, fingering the finely pleated nylon skirt doubtfully. No, it was not quite right for this evening, she decided, and hung it in the wardrobe. She would wear the lapis blue sun-dress, which would be far more suitable. It was sleeveless, with a low neckline, the bodice being held up merely by straps of the same material tied into little bows on the shoulders. She brushed her hair, sparingly used lip rouge and perfume, took a last look in the mirror, and went downstairs to the room to which she and Eric had been taken on their arrival. She had fully expected Eric to be there before her, but to her dismay she found herself alone with Carl. He was standing by a cocktail cabinet, but on her entry he swung round, his black eyes boring into her, as in total silence he waited for her to come farther into the room. This she did, haltingly, her anxious ears alert for the sound of her employer coming down the stairs. Carl had changed from the black slacks and roll-necked sweater into a pair of grey linen trousers and a white shirt. It was open at the neck and he wore no jacket. He was aware of her interest and she found herself colouring under his glacier-cold stare. With a supreme effort she escaped it to fix her attention on the view through the window.

The sun was sinking rapidly, transforming the brilliant colours of the garden to less spectacular hues of bronze and peach and coral rose. The incessant whirring of cicadas could be heard through the fly-netting over the open window, and the occasional overtone of a bird making for its nightly haven in the trees. Through these sounds came the mournful, plaintive bray of a donkey tethered on a lonely hillside.

'Would you like a drink, Sarah?' The low guttural voice made her jump, and although her recovery was swift, his sudden sneer revealed his perception. 'Sit down.' It was a command, and her chin lifted.

'I'd rather stand, if you don't mind.'

The black pitchblende eyes glinted dangerously. 'Sit down, Sarah.' So soft the words, but commanding. Her heart throbbed its submission, and she obeyed. But she was fuming. This is no way to treat a guest, she wanted to flash at him, but somehow her mouth and tongue were far too dry for speech.

'What do you drink these days . . .?' He stopped, then added, 'Seven years ago it was lemonade.'

'A dry martini, please,' she managed, not wanting a drink but feeling it was better not to refuse.

'You've become more sophisticated with the passing of the years,' he said, handing her the glass.

'I'm more mature, that's all.'

'A career girl?'

'Yes, a career girl.'

'Still determined not to marry, eh?'

She froze, every nerve tightened by the strange inflection in his voice and the black venom in his eyes. She knew even before his next words came that he was aware of her marriage.

'A widow who has retained her own name and

claims she's against marriage!' He spat out the sentence, coming closer as he spoke.

'Carl . . . I—'

'Why did you marry—only a matter of weeks after you'd refused me, telling me you would never marry?' He was far too close, towering above her, formidably threatening, apparently aware of the fact that he was putting fear into her and obviously enjoying his power.

'It was a necessity,' she began. 'You see—'

'He had more money than I,' he broke in with a snarl. 'You turned me down but you didn't know my great-uncle would die so soon, did you?' His face was contorted, his blind fury out of all proportion.

'I'm my own mistress,' she said stiffly. 'Captain of my own soul. I make my own decisions. I didn't want to marry you and I never led you on, you must agree with me about that.'

He said nothing, and she watched, fascinated, as he quaffed his whisky in one silent swallow, then held the glass in front of him, his fiery gaze fixed on its spirit-mottled sides.

'You married him for his money—'

'What makes you think that?' She twisted her head, listening again for Eric's footstep on the stairs.

'It was obvious. Only a few weeks . . . If only . . .' His roving eyes stripped her body, then settled on her face. 'You didn't collect any scars—but you didn't collect a fortune either; he left you nothing! What a bitter blow that must have been! Oh, yes, I know all about it,' he said on seeing her puzzled expression. 'I came over, because I wanted you so badly—I came to plead and beg and persuade! My God, I had no guts in those days! Would I plead now? *I shall take, get that!*' He was mad, she decided, staring up into eyes that were glazed. Yes, there was certainly something wrong with his mind . . . She slid to the edge of the chair when his head was turned the other way, with the intention of making her escape, but stopped, her pulses racing as his head came round again and his black eyes stared down at her, the directness of their gaze all-examining. 'No, you collected no scars by marrying, but I did—scars that will never fade! If you had married me, it never would have happened!'

'You're married?' she broke in, and a diabolical laugh rang out in response.

'She's dead!' His lips were drawn back against his teeth; his eyes were smouldering embers of hate. 'You—you're going to collect scars, though—yes, many scars before I've finished with you!' Sarah blanched, not knowing what was terrifying her most—Carl, or the wild pulsation of her heart that made her feel it was ready to burst.

'Your marriage,' she said through whitened lips, 'it . . . it d-didn't turn out w-well . . .?' She hadn't meant to say anything like that, but she scarcely had control of her mind, let alone her voice.

'It was hell!' Brooding, the voice now; and the harsh mouth quivered. 'She's dead . . . but she killed my child first.'

'Killed?'

He nodded. A greyish pallor had spread over his face, and his mouth worked spasmodically. Sarah could almost feel the agony that was crucifying him.

'She was mad. She was jealous of my love for Christos . . . little three-year-old Christos. . . .' His voice trailed away on a sob that came up from the depths of his heart. 'She killed him. . . .' He looked up and his voice broke into a snarl. 'It was your fault—do you hear!' Losing control altogether, he shot out a hand, savagely gripping her wrist, and she was jerked to her feet, the glass spinning from her nerveless fingers to spill its liquid over the carpet. 'He had more money—you turned me down for him! But your scheming came to nothing, didn't it? You got *nothing* for your trouble.' His satanic laugh rang out so loudly that Sarah was sure Eric would hear it and come running down to see what was happening. But her relief was not to come yet, not until her slender body had been crushed against his, her lips bruised as his ravishing mouth seared pain into hers. In the violence of her struggle a shoulder strap became caught in his fingers, and as she swung away it snapped, and one side of her bodice dropped. He stared at the half-exposed breast, held in the lacy bra, and Sarah feared he would seize her again and in a mad loss of control would hurt her unmercifully.

She was just about to scream in an endeavour to save herself when he said, with staggering composure and calm, 'You'd better see to that shoulder strap.'

Sarah was speechless. There was no sign of the passion that had possessed him. Not a trace of anger in his eyes. But nor was there any other emotion. His manner was dispassionate; he looked through her rather than at her. 'Your employer will be down directly, and I'm sure you don't want him to see you like that.'

She fumbled with the strap.

'I'll go and ch-change,' she quivered. 'I . . . I hope I don't bump into him . . . coming down the stairs.'

'I'll show you another stairway. It's used by my staff.'

In full command of himself now, he flicked a hand imperiously, beckoning her to follow him, which she did, thankful to be escaping from the room.

Chapter Three

Sarah spoke little during dinner, content to listen to the conversation going on between the two men. She had amazed herself by the way she had managed to regain control, even to the extent of being able to meet Eric with her usual cool confidence when she came down for the second time and entered the room to find him there, drinking an aperitif while talking to his host. Both men were standing, and although Eric was by no means a small man, Carl seemed to tower above him, an impressive figure despite the harsh, satanic lines of his face. She heard the business of the villa being discussed, fancied she detected an edge of indifference in Carl's voice, but told herself she must be mistaken. He was obviously keen to sell the house, for otherwise he would never have sent for a prospective purchaser.

Again, during dinner, when the business of the house was brought up by Eric, there seemed to be a total lack of interest on Carl's part. Impelled by an access of curiosity, Sarah asked Carl where the villa was situated.

'Here,' replied Carl non-committally, 'on Comaris.' His glance slid from her face to the delectable curves of her breasts, and she blushed at the memory of what had gone before. His mouth curved in a half-sneer that portrayed both mockery and contempt.

'You haven't said very much about this property.' Eric looked faintly anxious. 'Whereabouts on Comaris?'

'I did say that we would discuss business after dinner,' Carl reminded him curtly. 'Sarah will go to her room and leave us to discuss my proposition in private.' The cool tone of authority brought a sudden scowl to Eric's forehead, but he did not argue, or even comment. Sarah, sending Carl a glance from under her lashes, tried to read his expression, for there had been something strange and subtle in the content of his last words.

'. . . my proposition . . .'? It did not fit, somehow. . . . His previous words about her going to her room might at any other time have affected her temper, but not under the present circumstances. She would escape to her room now if it were at all possible.

The garden was clothed in the soft blanket of mothy darkness when, after bidding the men good night, she entered her bedroom and walked over to the window without switching on the light. It was so peaceful out there, a place to commune with oneself, to view a situation with crystal-clear vision. . . . Opening the window, she stepped out, standing for a space to listen to the night sounds—the cicadas in the olive trees, the croaking of frogs in the aquatic plants growing round an ornamental pool, the bray of the lonely donkey over on the hill—how sad it was! Why were people of the East so cruel to their animals? Donkeys were not meant to be fastened by a rope to a stake in the ground. They were meant to be free, but man in his greed had made prisoners of them, beasts of burden that he often did not even trouble to feed properly. Greed. . . . Yes, so much could be put down to greed, she mused, mechanically moving towards the steps which led from the verandah to the sun-terrace below her window. One could say that it was greed that had brought her employer here. Always it was a case of devising ways of making money, and it was not as though Eric really needed it. . . . Her mind wandered, and so did her steps. She was thinking about Eric and his recent expenditure cuts. Could it be that he had suffered some losses lately? If so, he had kept them from her, because she had not noticed any appreciable fall in business.

'But it's not like him to cut down just for the sake of it. . . .' Her steps brought her to the pool patio, and she sat down on one of the chairs, leaning her elbows on the small garden table. Her thoughts had switched, and she was concentrating on what she had been trying to avoid up till now—Carl, and his disclosure that he had been married. And it was this marriage that had made him what he was today—a fiend, almost. She wondered what the woman had been like, wondered about the child, his little three-year-old son. What was the manner of his death? Where did it happen, and when? More questions . . . all with no answers. She sighed, restless, and conscious of that nameless fear at the back of her mind all the time, troublesome, like the thread of a dream that escapes recall.

She sat there for a long while, the warm balmy air soothingly perfumed by flowers in the garden and from the pine-scented breeze floating down from the high places. What a paradise . . . with Carl such an incongruous owner. She instantly fell to thinking about him again, and of what his marriage had done to him. She thought that even years of solitary confinement in a prison cell could not have had an effect of such magnitude.

Her mind wandered, recapturing those days, seven years ago, when in love and adoration Carl had wooed her like a knight of old, almost. He was everything any girl could wish for, and if only she had not been so averse to marriage, she could easily have reciprocated, falling victim to his sincere, persuasive charm. Had she married him, he would never have suffered the heartbreaking experience that had wrought the change in him, and so, indirectly, *she* was to blame for what he was today, a man wounded in heart and mind, a man ravaged by a deep unconquerable mental agony.

Ice touched her heart, and she felt numbed; she rose and stood there in the starlight, a statue cold as stone. She closed her eyes, trying desperately to put a barrier between her vision and the dark, pagan face that persistently intruded into it. She opened them again and looked up at the sky, where peace was. The whole arc of the heavens was star-studded, and the sickle of a young moon hung suspended, argent and clear-cut against the deep purple sky of a Grecian night.

Suddenly every nerve in her body went taut, and the fine golden hairs of her forearms stiffened into life. A step on the gravel . . . a shadow flitting ominously against the trunk of a tree. She tried to turn and run, but her legs were pulp beneath her.

The shadow stopped, and Sarah could imagine its owner sniffing the air like some prowling jungle cat scenting its prey. The shadow came toward her, and a low guttural voice said, 'What are you doing here, Sarah? I told you to go to your room.' Carl was upon her, the hand that touched her cold as the grave. She shuddered and tried to swing away, but the grip on her wrist was tightened, and slowly, as if to torture her, Carl brought her protesting body close against his own. She twisted about in frantic resistance to the threat of his merciless mouth, but with his other hand he took a grip on her chin, jerking it up. 'Do you think you can escape me this time? I ought not to have let you escape before.' His head came down, his lips seeking her mouth.

'Don't!' she cried, pushing her hands against his chest. 'Get away from me! Where's Eric? Why aren't you with him—?' The rest was smothered by the iron-hard pressure of his lips. Her mouth was forced open and she made a little choking sound on feeling his tongue against her own. Why, oh why, hadn't she kept to the protection of her room? He would not have pursued her there.

'I lost my son,' he gritted, his vile mouth close to her ear, 'but you will replace him! You will give me what she took away!'

'You must be crazy!' Desperately she kicked out at his shin, but if he felt a stab of pain he had no intention of reacting to it in any way that would provide her with satisfaction. His hands were cruel on her arms as he held her from him, and even in the dimness she could make out the hard, almost bestial light in his eyes. She felt herself to be the captive of the devil, and she opened her mouth to scream. His hand trapped the cry before it left her lips, and as he pulled his hand away his sensuous mouth took over. When at last he had finished with her, she swayed in his arms, fury rising as, with terrible reluctance, she secretly owned to his having awakened emotions she never believed she possessed. She had almost reciprocated when his strong brown hands caressed where they should not have done, and his hungry lips found the warm soft curves of her breasts.

He looked down at her from his great height, laughed in her face and said triumphantly, 'Yes, my beautiful Sarah, you will give me the son I lost . . . and after that you'll be free—free to try your luck again!'

She managed to take him off guard and escape from his punishing grip.

'Where's Eric?' she quivered, marvelling that she could speak at all, afflicted as she was by physical and emotional fatigue. 'You haven't finished your business, surely?'

'It's settled to the satisfaction of us both.' Something in his voice brought Sarah's heart surging right up into her throat, its erratic pumping of blood through her veins making her feel dizzy and sick.

She was terrified, unable to shake off the heavy weight of doom that was pressing down upon her, and in the panic of despair she spoke optimistically, knowing it to be false. 'So we shall be leaving here tomorrow, then?'

Carl moved, his rubber-soled shoes noiseless on the marble flooring of the patio. He went slowly towards a vine-draped trellis forming part of the screen protecting the swimming pool. Reaching it, he turned, his tall figure vague in outline against the background of foliage, but she could see his face in starlight, darkly evil, like Satan.

'Your employer has already gone,' came the answer at last. 'You, Sarah, will be staying.'

Her heart stopped beating, then started again, its wild vibrations shaking her whole body from head to foot.

'No . . . wh-what d-did you say? Eric—he . . . can't have g-gone without me. . . .' She rushed past him, flying towards the house in frenzied haste, panic lending wings to her feet. 'Eric!' she shouted even before she reached the steps leading into the hall. 'Eric—where are you? Oh, for God's sake answer me!' She screamed his name, uncaring for the two menservants who had appeared from the back regions of the house, followed by the gaping Androula. 'Answer me, I say . . .' The words broke on a sob as she realised the futility of her cries. Carl had spoken the truth: Eric had left the island. . . .

Sarah turned as Carl entered the hall less than twenty seconds behind her. She saw him flick an imperious hand, the gesture ordering his servants to return to their own quarters.

'He's gone. . . .' Sarah's face was as white as chalk; her voice shook as her head moved from side to side. 'You made him go?'

'He left on my launch about half an hour ago. He should be halfway to Rhodes by now.' Carl leant against one of the tall white columns, his arms folded across his chest. 'He took a bribe, Sarah, and left you with me—'

'A bribe? I don't believe you! What kind of talk is that? Do you take me for an idiot? In any case, Eric doesn't need money.'

'Vernon is on the point of bankruptcy,' Carl informed her. 'He's been making some very bad investments during the past year— No, please don't interrupt,' he commanded as she opened her mouth to speak. 'I happen to have many business connections in London, and I go over fairly regularly. For many years I've kept track of what both you and he have been doing. He needed money badly, a circumstance that put power into my hands—'

'Why should you want power over Eric?' she flashed without thinking.

'Simply because I wanted power over you,' was the terse explanation. 'I've wanted revenge for a very long while, Sarah—ever since the day I discovered you'd refused my offer of marriage only to marry someone less worthy—but more wealthy—within a few short weeks.' His voice, quiet and controlled, was reminiscent of what it once had been, except that it lacked the gentle, tender tones which he had always used when speaking to her. 'Your employer appeared to think that your husband had left you his fortune . . .?' Carl looked interrogatingly at her, but she remained silent, so deeply interested in what he was saying that she almost forgot her own precarious position. 'I knew he had not left you a penny.' Carl went on.

But he got no further as Sarah interrupted him, asking casually, 'How did you know I'd been left nothing?'

'Your father told me. When I went over to England to try again to persuade you to marry me, I naturally went to your home, to the address you had given me. I saw your father—your mother wasn't in at the time. It was your father who told me you'd been married and that your husband was killed on your wedding day.' Carl stopped, and as she watched his face twist, she also saw tiny beads of perspiration ooze out of his skin, saw him raise a hand to his forehead to brush them away. 'I could scarcely take it in,' he continued, regaining his composure. 'I asked why you would marry when you'd declared emphatically that you were against marriage. Your father laughed and said it was for gain. The man was a millionaire and you'd married him to get hold of some of his money. . . .' His voice trailed as he noticed Sarah's expression. 'What's the matter?'

'My father said that?' she queried in disbelief.

'It's true,' he stated harshly, 'so don't deny it.'

'I wasn't intending to.' She spoke mechanically, scarcely aware of just what she had said. She had known her father was rotten, but never would she have believed he could have been as malicious as that. Perhaps it was understandable that he would be averse to telling the truth—that it was through him that she had been forced into a marriage she did not want—but he could at least have found some other excuse for her action.

'It was your father who told me you'd inherited nothing,' he said again, and laughed, as if it afforded him some amusement, 'that you'd done it all for nothing.'

'I see. I have a lot to thank my father for,' she quivered. 'He killed my mother . . .' She stopped, unwilling to enter into a subject intimately connected with her own life. Her father had recently re-married and was living abroad; she hoped she would never set eyes on him again as long as she lived.

'Did you tell this fellow Vernon that you'd come into the money?' Carl asked, watching her closely, peering into her very soul with those unfathomable black eyes of his.

'Can we cut out the irrelevancies,' she said tautly. 'I want to know why Eric has left the island without me.'

Carl's eyes glinted at her way of speaking, but he decided to let it pass, telling her instead that as Eric was almost bankrupt he had been more than willing to accept payment for leaving his secretary behind.

'He accepted payment—how much?'

'That's not your business,' he snapped. 'It was enough to see him out of his difficulties.'

'You never had a house for sale, then? You brought us here under false pretenses?'

'Correct. I wanted you. I'm at last able to have my revenge.' So calm, the voice, and unemotional. He might have been sharing a friendly conversation with her, had it not been for the content of his words.

'I can't believe that Eric would accept money for leaving me on the island.' But she could believe it, she was already admitting, for it was now plain why he had wanted to marry her. He had hoped to get his hands on the fortune that would solve all his money problems. And as he had failed, he had been unscrupulous enough to grasp this other way out of his difficulties.

'But he *has* left you on the island,' returned Carl smoothly. 'And there is no way you can get off it, until I let you.' His voice had changed to firmness, but the earlier harsh and guttural tones were still missing. 'There's no escape for you, Sarah, so I hope you'll resign yourself to the inevitable.'

She swallowed hard, but the terrible blockage of fear and despair remained. Nevertheless, she could not possibly accept defeat at this stage, nor was she intending to give him the satisfaction of seeing her fear.

'Is it likely that I'll resign myself to staying here?' she flashed. 'And do you suppose you can get away with holding me prisoner against my will? We live in a civilised world, and I'll be missed. Even though Eric manages to give some explanation to my colleagues for my leaving the firm, they're going to ask where I am. Many of them will want to write to me—'

'I'm quite sure, Sarah, that your employer will find some acceptable explanation for your disappearance. He's an ingenious young man, that one. I wouldn't trust him out of my sight, and it amazes me that you, having worked for him for so long, have never realised just what a scoundrel he could be.'

She looked away. She supposed she had taken Eric at his face value, considering herself to be his employee first, and his friend second. Always she had been conscious that he was her boss. It had not been her business to examine and analyse his character. His amorous pursuits were of course well known, not only to her but also to everyone working in the office. But as regards anything else—well, the fact that she had not known about his losses proved just how great the gap was between them.

'I have a sister,' she said after a while. 'She'll miss me and have inquiries made.'

'Vernon told me you are not very close, that you see one another only about twice a year.'

She bit her lip. 'Nevertheless, she's going to miss me sooner or later.'

'And the first person she will contact will be Vernon,' returned Carl reasonably. 'And he will have an answer.'

'Such as?'

Carl shook his head carelessly. 'How should I know? I've said he's a most ingenious young man. I imagine he'll find something feasible enough to be accepted by your sister.' A small pause, and then: 'If all goes well, you should be free to leave here in just about twelve months' time.' So casual the tone! But for her his remark meant embarrassment, and she felt the colour rise rapidly in her cheeks. His eyes, still darkly pagan, were yet amused, and faintly mocking.

'I *shall* escape!' she seethed. 'How can you keep me here against my will? What about your servants? I can ask them to help me.' Even as she spoke, she was doubting the strength of her assertion, for on an island like this it would be foolhardy for any servant to risk losing his or her job.

As if reading her thoughts, Carl was smiling to himself. 'My servants know better than to do anything to arouse my displeasure,' he calmly assured her.

'The people in the village—some of them must have boats. . . .' Her voice faded to silence as he began to shake his head.

'I own the only ferry boat that operates between here and Rhodes.'

'You?' She frowned. 'No one other then you owns a boat here?' This ferry must be in addition to the luxury launch which brought her and Eric from Rhodes, she mused.

'There are fishing boats, of course, but they stay around our shores. They're not equipped for a long trip.'

'There's only one boat, and it's yours?' She shook her head in disbelief.

'It began when my great-uncle first bought Comaris and came to live here. He provided a boat for the use of the people who, until then, scarcely ever left the island, but in order to keep Comaris totally private, he made a law that no one other than himself could own a boat. Times are changing and I'm thinking of allowing those who want their own boats to have them.' He paused significantly. 'But for the present the old law made by my great-uncle will remain.' Again he paused, briefly; then: 'The ferry sails once a week and is manned by my crew. They shall be given orders never to take you on board.'

'So I really am a prisoner,' she said flatly.

'Yes, Sarah, you are. My prisoner. You'll be released when you've given me what I demand as reparation—a son.'

Chapter Four

The golden glow of dawn was filtering through the gaps in the long brocatelle drapes as Sarah opened her eyes. Fleetingly the unfamiliar aspect puzzled her, until her subconscious flashed comprehension into her brain. She jerked to a sitting position, every detail of the previous night's events crowding in on her, overtaxing her mind until she wanted to stand up and scream.

But with a determined effort she remained calm, her common sense telling her that nothing could be more unprofitable in this dire situation than hysterics.

At least she had escaped Carl's amorous intentions last night when, his threats having broken her completely, she succumbed to a fit of weeping, which, racking her whole body, had by some miracle brought forth the totally unexpected words: 'Go to bed. You're all in. We'll talk some more in the morning,' and with that he had gone from her bedroom, leaving her unharmed physically but drained to the depths mentally.

She had lain awake, but not for long. Nature had taken over, providing her with the strength to rise from her bed this morning fit and ready to do battle with her captor.

She took a shower and felt even more refreshed, but she wished she had brought a better supply of clothes. She would ask Androula for a needle and thread later, so that she could mend the strap on the blue dress; meanwhile she had no choice but to wear the one she had worn for dinner, a lilac linen sun-dress, low-cut and sleeveless like the other one, but with something more substantial than shoulder straps to hold up the bodice. What, she wondered, would today bring? There was nothing fixed in her mind, just the desperate hope that something would turn up to prevent Carl carrying out his diabolical intentions.

He was in the breakfast room when she entered, taken there by Androula, who eyed her with an odd expression, and Sarah was reminded of the innate curiosity of the Greeks, which often proved most disconcerting to foreigners. There was nothing malicious in it—on the contrary. They were merely interested, although in Androula's particular case, it was obviously something more than mere interest that was in her eyes at the present time. She had witnessed a scene of near-hysteria last night and it was to be expected that she and the two men were very curious indeed to know what it was all about.

'Good morning, Sarah,' Carl greeted her. 'Did you

sleep well?' The black eyes roved before settling on her face. 'You're looking fine, so you must have slept. Sit down; breakfast will be here directly.' He clapped his hands to bring a manservant into the room.

'You can serve breakfast now,' said Carl.

'Very good, Mr Carlos.' A covert look was cast in Sarah's direction before the man went out.

Carl's glance flicked her attire. 'I don't suppose you brought many clothes with you,' he commented. 'We. must get you some. Comaris is a small island, but very civilised. Theodora has a smart ladies' shop in the village. You can go down and order what you want and tell her to send the bill to me.'

Sarah set her teeth, but, determined to keep calm, she sat down at the table and leant back in a manner of deceptive ease.

'I shan't require your clothes,' she said. 'You must know you can't keep me here. There are many other people living on the island; there must be someone who will help me—'

'No, Sarah,' he broke in softly. 'You've forgotten one thing, the most important thing. I am master of this island; we have an almost feudal society. here on Comaris, and I am the seigneur. My word is law. But in any case, you can't leave without a boat, and I've told you that the only ferry boat is mine.' He was still standing, tall and gaunt and formidable, and Sarah had to admit that he looked the part of an all-powerful seigneur, master of all he surveyed. 'No, Sarah, there will be no escape for you until I myself let you go. It's only a year, after all, so why not resign yourself at the outset? It will be so much more comfortable, I can assure you of that.'

He sat opposite to her, turning his head slightly as

Yannis entered carrying a silver tray on which there were two crystal bowls containing fresh grapefruit. These he placed on the table, serving Carl first.

'Thank you.' Carl's voice was abrupt; the man inclined his head and went out.

Sarah's blue eyes dropped to the fruit; it was strange, but she was ready to tackle a hearty breakfast, and this was something she had certainly not expected!

'More comfortable,' she repeated when the man had gone. 'Is that a threat?'

'I'm advising you to accept your fate.' Picking up his spoon, he dug it into the grapefruit. She looked at his dark head, noticing the threads of iron-grey hair, but noticing too that it was still thick, and the wave he had once seemed so bent on straightening out had been allowed to go its own natural way.

She took up her spoon and began to eat her fruit. Carl was speaking again, into the silence that had fallen between them. If she gave him too much trouble, he said, he would keep her confined to the house and the grounds around it.

'How could you do that?' she asked.

'My servants would watch you.'

'I see.' She was not surprised by his answer. A man as determined as Carl would see to it that she never escaped until she had given him what he wanted—a son.

He fell silent, and Sarah became thoughtful, her brain working furiously. There must be some way out of this, her subconscious was saying, some means of escape which had not yet occurred to her. And then, right out of the blue it flashed into her mind. A letter! There must be a post-box on the island and a place where stamps could be bought. The letters would go by ferry to Rhodes, and then hers would go to her sister in London. . . .

'What are you thinking about, Sarah?' she heard him say in a very soft voice.

'Nothing.' She spoke swiftly, the high-pitched note in her voice the result of optimism. 'Why do you ask?'

His eyes narrowed slowly, and she felt that by the very gesture he could crush every vestige of hope out of her.

'If you're thinking of sending a letter,' he said in the same soft tone of voice, 'then forget it. All letters are collected from the box by one of my men, who takes them to the ferry. I'm giving orders that, until further notice, all letters are to be brought to me for examination before being taken on the ferry. In a few minutes you shall give me a sample of your handwriting—'

'All right!' she broke in, tears of disappointment clouding the backs of her eyes, 'you needn't go any further. I understand—perfectly!'

'I thought you would,' was his suave rejoinder before, casually, he continued eating his breakfast. Then, as they were about to finish their meal, he spoke again, but if what he had had to say before had been a disappointment to Sarah, what he had to say now was devastating.

'We shall be married this afternoon. I've already telephoned my friend the priest—'

'You must be mad!' she burst out. 'I've no more intention of marrying you now than I had seven years ago!'

His black eyes narrowed dangerously, and Sarah moistened her lips, an unpleasant tightness settling in her throat. She ought to have had more sense than to remind him of what happened seven years ago.

'It's marriage . . . or else,' he said slowly. 'I believe
you'll prefer marriage. Most women would, under the
circumstances.'

Colour flooded her cheeks at the allusion contained
in the last sentence, but although her fury rose, she
was determined to retain her outward calm.

'You're giving me an ultimatum?'

'Call it what you like. I'd prefer my son to be
legitimate, though.'

She lifted her eyes to his, noting the rock-hardness
in their depths, the inflexibility in their stare. And
with terrible reluctance she admitted she was beaten.
Betrayed by Eric, whose greed for money had resulted
in his leaving her on this island with a man whose
dominance was absolute, she could see no possible
way of escape. Marriage . . . or else. . . . She swallowed the saliva that had filled her mouth, pushing
the bowl of fruit to one side. Her appetite had gone.

Carl was standing by the bathroom door, a formidably tall figure, harsh of feature, eyes brooding in some
strange unfathomable way that made Sarah think of
the past . . . and what their wedding night might
have been if only she had been able to accept her
handsome lover's offer of marriage. Was Carl recalling
memories too, and dwelling on what might have
been? Some inexplicable tremor fluttered near her
heart—a sensation she could neither understand nor
explain.

'Must you stand there, watching me?' she said,
breaking into a silence that had become unbearable.
'You needn't have come yet.' She picked up a hair-
brush from the dressing-table, but merely stared
fixedly at the silver etching on the back of it. Carl, in a
dressing-gown of black satin with fiery red dragons

spreading their patterned talons down the front and sleeves, had come into the bedroom, and now he was obviously intending to enjoy the spectacle of seeing his reluctant bride disrobe, but she was still fully dressed even though he had entered the room, from the one adjoining, several minutes ago. 'Can't I have some privacy?' She ought to be putting up some form of resistance, she thought, but the idea of the humiliation she would suffer in the process was far too daunting. For no matter what courage she should portray, defeat was inevitable. Better not to fight than to fight and lose and be brought down to the very depths of total submission. There was still one small victory that could be hers, though; she would never give him either the pleasure or the satisfaction of winning her reciprocation, she decided. But how little she knew. . . .

'Privacy?' with a lift of his straight black brows. 'You're my wife, Sarah. Why should you need privacy?'

She sent him a baleful glance. 'We might be married, but we're strangers,' she reminded him, at which he laughed softly and said that this would soon be remedied. 'I hate you,' she whispered.

'That makes two of us. I've hated you since the moment your father told me you'd married someone else—married not for love, but for money.'

She put down the brush, meeting his hard eyes through the mirror. Should she tell him the truth? And if she did, would he believe her? Sarah shrugged the questions aside, profoundly aware that whatever she said in her own defence would fall on deaf ears. She was in the hands of a fiend, a man without mercy who would have his way with her no matter what she did.

'Would you like some help?' he was saying gently. 'I

shall enjoy undressing you, Sarah. . . .' His voice drifted to threatening silence as he moved slowly towards her, his pagan eyes already stripping her. 'I said you hadn't changed much,' he added, coming to a halt as she backed away from him. 'But you have, just a little. Your curves are more mature . . . and more exquisitely desirable—'

'Shut up! Seeing that it's to be no more than what would happen between a man and woman who's been picked up on the street, you can cut out the trappings!'

'You—!' Fire blazed to life in his eyes, then died, indicating his intention of keeping a rein on his temper. 'I dislike intensely your particular turn of phrase, Sarah. Don't dare say anything like that again!'

'Isn't it only what would happen between two—'

'No, it is not! We're husband and wife! In Greece a woman would not dare to speak to her husband the way you are speaking.' He paused, anger giving strength to his breathing. 'Are you going to take off that dress, or am I?' he added, moving once more in her direction. She backed away until her legs touched the bed, her eyes dark with fear as they looked into his. He came on, untying his dressing-gown. It came open and she saw the black covering of dark curling hair on his chest. An animal, she thought, and shuddered. He took hold of her by the shoulders, pulling her to him; automatically she pressed her clenched fists against the hardness of his chest, resisting when she had already told herself she would not do so. It was instinctive, though, she realised when, his mouth touching hers, she began to struggle in earnest. But his encircling arms were bands of steel, inflexible and cruel. His mouth crushed hers with all the savagery of primitive passion, forcing her lips to part, his domi-

nance manifested in every sensuous movement of his
long lean frame. With a violent twist she broke free,
staggering from him on legs that seemed almost to
have lost their function of supporting her. With a
pounding heart she tried to reach the door, but he
caught hold of her dress, ruthlessly jerking her back
towards the bed. Securing both her hands in one of
his, he unzipped her dress; she seized the opportunity
of struggling again when he was forced to release her
hands to slip the dress from her shoulders, but the
respite was fleeting. He gripped her hands again, his
eyes roving her scantily clad frame for a long moment
before she was swung against his chest. Wild with
fury and hate, she tried to combat the powerful
animal strength of him, sobs escaping all the time
from the very depths of a heart that was pounding
madly against her ribs.

'Stop struggling!' he commanded at last, obviously
coming to the end of his patience. 'A Greek wife would
be beaten for less than this!' He was unclipping her
bra as he spoke. It came away in his hand.

'I'm n-not a Greek . . . wife. . . .' She was crying
now, quietly, her white face upraised. 'Please let me
go . . .' She stopped, sagging against the coiled-spring
hardness of his body. 'I hate you,' she whispered, 'hate
you with everything in me.'

'Hate away,' he snarled, the fire of his passion
re-ignited by the lovely vision she made in the one
scanty garment he had not yet removed. She felt his
hot breath on her throat, then the torture of his mouth
as it took brutal possession of her lips while a hand
sought the firm contour of her breast, cupping it,
caressing but not gently, tantalising every nerve in
her body by the slow pinching of the nipple between
his fingers. There was sensuality in everything he did,

even in the way he looked into her eyes, seeking for the dark glaze that would tell him of her aroused emotions. She brought her head down to avoid a gaze that could read her very soul, then uttered a little cry of pain as he took a handful of hair to jerk her head back again.

'Don't avoid my eyes,' he ordered arrogantly. 'I want to see into yours! I enjoy the anguish, but I enjoy the surrender more!' The curve of his mouth was a sneer tinged with contempt. 'Your eyes are cloudy with desire for me, and yet your heart is cold with hate! Do you realise what satisfaction you're giving me—do you?' She swayed as he held her from him, his tone of voice an imperious command for her to answer him.

'I . . . I h-have an idea,' she quavered.

'Yes?' She had lowered her head, but a rough hand beneath her chin brought it up again.

'I suppose it's . . . it's triumph.' She was meek only because of exhaustion and fear. In her slender body there was no strength left, and in her heart was fear.

'How right you are—it's triumph. But it's retribution as well—a paying back for the hell I've been through since you turned me down. It never dawned on you that, one day, I'd have you in my power, did it? I've waited for this hour, waited for the recompense I intend to have from you!'

'You're nothing but a fiend!' She renewed her struggles, but he took advantage of her movements to meld her body with his own, and a cloud of black fury and hatred almost suffocated her when his arrogant, possessive hand slid right down into the one tantalising scrap she wore, its pressure forcing her body into an arched position, bringing her loins so close that she was compelled to experience the nauseating hardness of his virility. His other hand left her breast to remove the one remaining garment, and in seconds she was standing naked before him, her cheeks crimson, her mouth twisting convulsively. He was holding her at a distance from him, his eyes seeming to be fascinated by the gentle swell and fall of her stomach. He touched it, then encircled her within his arms again, bringing her close, uniting her flesh with his. A shudder of disgust rippled through her, while the dizzy heights of her awakened emotions beckoned her irresistibly. He lifted her, and she cringed, turning from him as he laid her down on the bed. But her little demonstration of defiance was pathetic. Carl laughed at it as with arrogant mastery he turned her towards him when he lay down beside her. His hands roved, and within seconds fire was licking her veins and with a little moan of ecstasy that was meant to be despair, she surrendered to the mastery of the man who had waited years for his revenge.

Chapter Five

It was with a sense of shock that Sarah awoke to find herself alone. Carl had left her sometime during the night. . . .

For no reason that she could explain, she felt her colour rise with embarrassment and humiliation. He had left her, and she was glad! She hoped he would always leave her. She sat up in bed, her eyes sliding to the connecting door, which was firmly closed. Was he still sleeping? she wondered, her mind going back to yesterday and the coming to the house of the priest from the village. A friend of Carl's, he was delighted to be performing the ceremony. To Sarah he was nothing more nor less than an old reprobate, hiding his sensual leanings benind a long grey-white beard and a benign smile—or was it a snigger that she saw when, after the wedding in the lounge of Carl's house, he said something in Greek to his friend, while his leering glance stripped the bride naked. Sarah had harboured a glimmer of hope until she saw the priest, feeling that she might have an opportunity of whispering to him, of telling him of her plight. But one look at his face and she decided she would not trust him as far as she could throw him. There would be no help from that quarter, and as there was no one else to whom she could turn either, Sarah resigned herself to her fate, hoping she would have the child in less than a year so that she could make her escape from this island, and from Greece, a country she never wished to set foot in again as long as she lived. She thought of Eric and of what she would have to say to him on her return to England; she thought of her flat, standing empty, of the people in the other flats with whom she had been on speaking terms, and who would naturally wonder where she was. So many things to trouble her mind, but all seemed as nothing beside the life she was compelled to endure until she presented her husband with a son.

She slid from the bed and got into a négligé. The dawn in all its glory was shedding its copper-gold glow over the gardens as she drew back the drapes. Beauty and peace everywhere. . . . Her eyes brooded as she stared, one half of her mind telling the other half to forget what had happened last night because if she dwelt on it her life would be sheer misery, with no diversions to mitigate the horror of the nights.

If she were to keep sane, then she must have diversions, even if they were only like this—watching the dawn when the great ball of the sun rose over the horizon. Dawn. . . . Like the breathless hush before the world awakes, like the beginnings of time before man—or even nature—stole into the universe from nowhere. So silent . . . and still, with not even the zephyr of a breeze to stir the silver olive leaves or the spidery palm fronds along the shore. So peaceful. . . .

Tears behind her eyes, and yet courage in her heart; despair and optimism mingling incongruously; a dozen other emotions too vague for analysing. . . . She opened the window and stepped out into the crisp morning air, where the cool was, and the perfume and the promise of a blue-sky day. She stood on the verandah and continued to watch the sun appear over the rim of the earth. Her eyes scanned the hills as their individual shapes came into focus in the rising light. The world around her was suddenly awake, vibrating with life. Colours and images became sharp and pure, and the air was filled with the heady scent of growing things. Vibrant colours—yellows and opals and jonquil-gold replacing the sombre hues of night. Bluffs on the hillsides were spangled with gold, while the hollows took on every shade of green in the play of light as a gossamer film of cirrus cloud swirled across the sun.

She looked down at the village of Phylia nestling between hills and shore, its white and blue cubic houses clustered round the church. There were shops where all necessities could be bought, and a little harbour where the ferry boat was moored, and her husband's launch. Little caïques were sailing in with the night's catch of fish, and even as Sarah watched, a stocky Greek in black pants and a polo-necked jersey leapt ashore, carrying an octopus which he began slapping on the pavement, creating the frothy white lather necessary for tenderising the fish.

In another direction could be seen a woman in black, driving her goats into the hills, where they would graze until dusk, when she would drive them back to her little farm for the night.

At last Sarah turned, to re-enter the bedroom. It was still very early, and after having a bath she dressed in a white cotton dress—a shirt-waister which Carl had had sent up from Theodora's shop yesterday, along with numerous other clothes. It had a high pointed collar and long sleeves gathered into tight cuffs. Nipped in to fit her tiny waist, it had a wide belt of navy blue leather to match the thonging which laced the front of the bodice. She looked exceedingly attractive in it, but a sigh escaped her. What would she give to put back the clock for a mere four days!—no, three would do, she realised with a sudden shock. Was it possible that so much had happened in such a short time?

It was still only half-past seven when she was again stepping onto the verandah with the intention of taking a stroll in the grounds of the villa, succumbing to the desperate need to do something to stop her dwelling on what had happened last night. She felt she would go mad if she brooded for too long at a time, and although she was well aware that a walk in the gardens would not be of any great help, at least it would be a little. Anything was better than sitting in the bedroom, thinking . . . recalling . . . reliving . . .

After wandering through the grounds she eventually found herself on the beach. It was isolated, the palms sentinel-still against the sky, the sea smooth as silk. She realised that there was no boundary line between Carl's private beach and the long length of pink-white sand that stretched for about a mile before it was lost to view by the intrusion of a rocky cliff which came right down to the sea. She walked on for six or seven minutes, then came suddenly upon a pretty sight that made her stop. Standing back from the shore, its gardens brights with flowers, was a small blue-shuttered villa surrounded on three sides by trees. What an idyllic spot! Whoever lived there didn't appear to be up yet, for the shutters were closed. She moved on but had covered only a few yards when someone called, 'Kalimera! It's a lovely morning!'

An English voice! Sarah stopped and turned. A fair-haired young man of medium height had come from somewhere behind the villa and was standing on the path leading from the house to the beach.

'Good morning,' returned Sarah. 'You're English?'

'So are you, I didn't know when I called, and I thought you might not understand English—but most people here speak our language, I was told.' He gave a laugh and began to move at the same time as she did. They met at the little gate and he said, 'Are you on holiday too?'

'No . . . er . . . are you on holiday?'

'For a month. My aunt and I have exchanged accommodation. She wanted to see life in her old age, and she's gone to London—taken over my flat.' There was no mistaking the admiration in his eyes as they settled on her face. 'I've a month's vacation every year, and I decided to take it all at once. You see, I've been looking for an opportunity to read all those books I can never get down to, and this seemed an ideal oppor-

tunity . . .' He broke off, giving a little self-dep-
recating laugh. 'I don't know why I'm telling a
stranger all this,' he went on ruefully, 'unless it's
because I haven't spoken to a soul since coming here
five days ago. Aunt Maroula met me at the harbour
and brought me here, and then went off on the next
ferry. She has a little car, which she uses for shopping
and to take her to the ferry. She needs it, I reckon, for
this house is what I would call isolated. Oh, Lord, I'm
at it again, talking my head off—'

'Don't apologise,' Sarah broke in, smiling. 'It's
marvellous to find one of my own countrymen to talk
to.'

He looked at her curiously.

'You're not on holiday, you say. But you don't live
here, surely?'

She hesitated, aware that her heart was beating
rather more quickly than was normal. An Englishman
who would be returning to England in less than a
month. . . . Was it possible that he could help her
escape? At least he could post a letter to her sister.

'Yes, I do. . . .' She pointed to the stately white villa
overlooking the sea. 'There.'

His eyes opened wide. 'That's the home of the man
who owns this island. My aunt told me he's strange—
the result of a tragedy. Do you work there or something?' he added, puzzled.

Again she hesitated, loath to tell him who she was,
yet at the same time aware that he had only to go into
the village and someone would be bound to mention
in passing that an English girl was living not far from
his aunt's house. Sarah supposed that gossip was rife
concerning the hasty marriage of the island's owner,
and the village shops would be the very place to hear
all about it.

'I'm married to Carl Duris,' she said at last, and heard his gasp of disbelief.

'Married to Carl Duris? But my aunt never mentioned a wife.'

'I was married only yesterday,' she said.

'Only yesterday?' His eyebrows lifted. 'Are you pulling my leg?' he asked suspiciously.

'No, it's the truth. I was married at three o'clock yesterday afternoon.' She was embarrassed, and so was he. She supposed his embarrassment was due to the fact that he had said her husband was strange.

'Yesterday, and you're here, alone, at eight o'clock in the morning? It doesn't make sense to me. Are you sure you're not having me on?'

Sarah shook her head. 'I'm speaking the truth,' she said.

The dejection in her voice could not possibly escape him, and for a long moment he stared at her, obviously at a loss. Eventually he said, 'Well, if you'll excuse me I'll be going—'

'You're doing everything for yourself?' she cut in hastily, wanting to keep him.

'Yes, Aunt Maroula has a small freezer, and she stocked it for me. I might have to go the the shops eventually, of course, for bread and one or two other things.' He now seemed in no hurry to leave her, she noticed, and wondered if he had realised that her swift interruption was an invitation for him to stay with her for a while. He must be exceedingly puzzled, and Sarah suspected that if she stayed too long he would be unable to contain his curiosity and might ask her outright if there was anything wrong. Even as it was, he could not help saying, 'You must forgive me if I'm looking at you a little strangely. You see, it's so early in

the morning . . . and you married only yesterday . . .'
He shrugged, as if he would have liked to add more
but good manners forbade it.

'I like walking early in the morning,' she said,
managing a smile. 'My husband's still asleep, and so I
seized the opportunity to come out and explore the
beach. . . .' Her voice trailed off lamely as she saw his
expression. 'I really do like walking early in the
morning,' she added defensively.

His expression was a study as he said, 'So you're not
rushing back just yet?'

'No—I think I shall go farther along here. Is it
possible to get round that cliff?'

'Yes. There's a footway to the beach at the other
side.' He hesitated; and then: 'Why not have a cup of
coffee with me instead? I was just going to make one
when I decided to have a wander round my aunt's
garden first, to smell the sunrise—'

'Smell the sunrise?' she echoed, diverted.

He nodded. 'There are fascinating smells when the
sun's coming up—but if you're used to being out early,
you must have noticed. The smells are there no matter
what part of the world you happen to be in, although
they vary, of course.' He was lifting the latch and he
swept an inviting hand as the gate swung inwards. 'If
you want to get the smells at their best, you should be
out when the sun's first coming over the horizon. The
whole atmosphere's intoxicating.'

'I saw the sun come over the horizon this morning . . .' She stopped, chiding herself for the slip.
No wonder his blue-grey eyes were open to their
fullest extent! But he let her words pass without
comment, and she mentally thanked him for it.

'I think we ought to exchange names,' he was

saying a few minutes later, when, after showing her
into the sitting-room, he said he would go and make
the coffee. 'Mine's Matthew—Johnson's the surname.'

'I'm Sarah,'

'Can I call you that?'

'Yes, of course.'

'I'll make the coffee,' he said again, and disap-
peared.

She glanced around. It was a small room at the back
of the house, and although here the shutters were
open the light was dim, the windows being rather
small and in addition heavily curtained with a thick
tapestry material. On the sideboard were all kinds of
bric-a-brac and two ancient icons with partly burned
candles in their holders close by them. Another, larger
icon hung on one wall, and beneath it, on a table, a
three-branch candelabra with unused white candles.
The furniture was old but good, the rugs on the tiled
floor hand-made. It was a homely room, and snug, but
in some indefinable way, depressing. Sarah thought it
must be the icons, and she was suddenly struck by the
absence of them in her husband's house. Perhaps, she
mused, he no longer believed in God.

Matthew returned with a small tray holding two
cups of coffee and a sugar bowl.

'I've made it milky without asking,' he said, 'but if
you don't like milk, I'll make you another.'

'I do like milk, but I don't take sugar.'

'Troubled about the calories?' His appreciative
glance examined a figure that was as nearly perfect as
possible. 'You've no need to worry about such things.'

'I don't; it's just that I dislike sugar in coffee.' She
leant back in the chair, marvelling at the way she was
able to relax, and concluded it was owing to the
prospect of freedom, for she was confident that

Matthew would post a letter for her in England. He was bound to think it strange, because Comaris was by no means cut off—on the contrary, letters were taken on the ferry to Rhodes and posted there, so some sort of explanation would be necessary when she asked Matthew to post her letter. However, Sarah decided to cross that bridge when she came to it, there being three weeks before Matthew left the island.

This time yesterday she was hoping and praying that the child Carl wanted would soon be on its way; she now regarded conception as a disaster. Either way, though, she would seize the opportunity of escape if it should arise.

Over the coffee their conversation was light and inconsequential, but Matthew's underlying curiosity and puzzlement were obvious, and Sarah half-expected him to ask some of the questions which were circling about in his mind. However, to her relief, he practised restraint, and only when she was leaving did he say, regarding her with an odd expression, 'Shall you be coming this way again tomorrow—at the same time?'

'Yes, I shall.'

The blue-grey eyes flickered. 'You'll come for coffee?'

'If you want me to.'

'It'll make an enjoyable start to my day.'

'I don't want to keep you from your reading,' she said.

'I don't get down to it until after nine. I've the household chores to do first. Aunt Maroula said I wasn't to leave everything until the last couple of days. A house ought to be cleaned every day, or else it gets out of hand.' He stopped and laughed, asking Sarah if she knew what that meant.

'No,' she admitted, 'I don't—not really. I expect your aunt is one of those ladies who follow a routine of doing the tidying up every day. When I was in my flat I often left all the jobs until the week-end, especially if I was going out in the evenings.'

'You were living on your own, then?'

'Yes,' briefly, before she added, 'Good-bye for the present. I'll see you tomorrow.'

'I'll be watching out for you,' he promised, and walked to the gate with her. As she heard the latch click behind her she knew instinctively that Matthew would stand there until she was out of sight, and she wondered what his thoughts were.

On entering the villa by the door opening onto the terrace, Sarah was immediately informed by Androula that breakfast was ready and that Carl was waiting.

'Thank you.' Sarah made for the morning-room, determined to hide any embarrassment she was feeling as to the events of last night.

Carl was standing by the window looking out, and he swung round quickly on hearing her come into the room, a frown on his brow. He looked evil, she thought, wondering whether he wore black for effect or because he liked it.

'Where have you been?' he demanded, looking her over as if he expected to find the answer written somewhere on her person.

'I've been walking.'

'Not on the grounds. I looked for you.'

'On the beach.' Somehow the meeting with Matthew had given her confidence, probably because of the optimism she felt about an early escape from her husband's clutches. 'You did not tell me there were to be any restrictions on my movements.'

Carl's eyes glinted dangerously. 'I advise you not to

adopt that attitude with me,' he said unpleasantly. 'It behooves you to remember who I am.' The quiet vibrancy in his voice betrayed suppressed anger; it also made the accent seem more pronounced.

Sarah's chin went up. 'And who *are* you?' she asked with chill sarcasm.

'Your husband . . . and your master. You're in Greece now—and you'll conform to the customs of my country. Here, the husband has full authority over his wife.'

Sarah's teeth snapped together. 'I'm English! You'll never make me into a submissive slave, so don't waste your time!'

To her surprise, he seemed taken aback by her attitude, and it was obvious that he was puzzled. She must be careful, she decided. If she went too far, he might be shrewd enough to suspect that there was a good reason for her defiance.

'Sit down—' He flicked a hand towards a chair, and she moved to take possession of it. 'Last night you were my submissive slave,' he said quietly and with a sneer.

She glowered at him, blushing hotly and trying to speak. But the tight little ball that had lodged in her throat choked back the words, and all that came through was a hiss of white-hot fury. Carl laughed as he sat down opposite to her at the table, a gaunt, straight-shouldered figure like something out of a lawless, bygone age, she thought, hating him with a black venom. What a victory for her if she should make her escape! She had worked nothing out yet, nor tried to visualise what would be the outcome of the letter she would send to her sister, but yet there was a feeling of optimism within her which was affecting her whole attitude towards the man who firmly believed he had her fully in his power until she gave him what he wanted.

It was Androula who brought the tray and silently served the grapefruit.

'What do you do with yourself all day?' she was asking Carl after a long silence. 'Do you have an office in Athens?' His great-uncle had had spacious offices in the capital, she recalled, and wondered if Carl had still retained them.

'Yes, but I rarely go there.' His voice brooded, his eyes were dark and unfathomable. 'I work here, in my study.'

'And I . . . ? What shall I do with my time?'

'I expect you'll find something,' he replied indifferently. 'There are many books, in English, in my library.'

'I can go down to the village? There are no restrictions on my movements over the island?'

'None. You can go where you like so long as you're here at meal times—and make sure you're prompt,' he added imperiously. 'I'm not intending to be kept waiting, as I was just now.'

Sarah seethed but said nothing at present. She had a certain amount of freedom, and she wanted to keep it.

The following morning Sarah awoke to find that, as before, Carl had left the bed sometime during the night. How stealthily he must move! she thought, marvelling that she could sleep as soundly as she did. Evidently her husband was not so fortunate—and she was glad! Perhaps, she mused, his conscience had begun to prick him. She doubted it, though, doubted that he had any conscience at all.

She herself had wakened a little later than yesterday, so she hurried with her bath, slipped into slacks and a blouse, brushed her hair and went out. Two gardeners were already at work in the borders, and as she passed them they both greeted her with smiles that revealed bright gold fillings.

'*Kalimera*, Mrs Carlos!'

'*Kalimera*,' she replied, and hurried on, towards the place beyond the trees where her husband's gardens extended to the beach. She found herself glancing around now and then, making sure she was not watched or followed.

Matthew was at the gate, smiling a welcome even before he bade her good morning.

'You're certainly up with the lark,' he said, opening the gate for her to pass through. 'I've got the coffee made already, in the percolator.'

'Lovely.' She preceded him into the sitting-room and sat down on the couch. Matthew stood for a moment, looking at her, his expression one of extreme puzzlement, and she decided at once not to come tomorrow, or the next day, because if she did, they would become friendly and he might then take the liberty of asking her questions which she was not willing to answer.

A few minutes later he had brought the coffee and they sat on the patio drinking it. All around them was shelter provided by trees and flowering bushes. She felt safe in this little haven a long way from any other house—safe and relaxed and at peace. Matthew talked about the books he had been reading, and as she had read some of them, they could exchange opinions. But all the time Sarah was guarded, careful not to drop her veil of reserve.

When they had finished discussing one particularly good novel, Matthew talked a little about himself, telling her that he lived alone in a small flat, and that he was an articled clerk in a firm of accountants. He had been engaged once but then jilted. It hurt at the time, but he decided he could not let it blight his life indefinitely. He had parents who, a year ago, on the retirement of his father, had immigrated to Canada to be near their married daughter. He had several hobbies, including stamp-collecting.

'And that's about it.' He grinned. 'Not an exciting life, but smooth—no complications.'

She looked swiftly at him, aware of the subtlety of the last word, but she could forgive him for his curiosity.

She rose to leave, regretfully shaking her head when he asked if she would be coming this way again tomorrow.

'I can't leave my husband every morning,' she returned, managing to laugh. But because she wanted to keep in touch with him, she said she would probably be taking a walk along the beach later in the week.

'You'll call for coffee?' His eyes were admiring as they swept over her figure.

'Yes, and thank you for asking me.'

'My pleasure,' he assured her. 'I like my own company, especially as I've come here to relax totally and read, but it's nice to have a chat now and then.' He walked to the gate with her and opened it. She smiled and tried to look happy as she bade him good-bye.

'Good-bye,' he responded. 'I shall probably see you about Friday or Saturday?'

'Yes . . . perhaps.'

Her voice was flat, but he did not seem to notice. She was wishing that the morning visits for coffee could become regular ones, bringing bright interludes into a life that was already monotonous and threatened to get worse. She had no one other than her husband to talk to, and that was only at meal times and at night. The servants extended a greeting in the morning, then nothing more. Sometimes they would look at her covertly through puzzled eyes. She knew they had been told nothing by the man employing them, nor would they ever dare to ask even the most superficial question. Androula, who did the bedroom, had left immediately when Sarah entered. Had Carl told her not to stay? Sarah suspected this was so; he was making sure that the girl did not talk to her new mistress. As for Carl, he was morose, and their meals yesterday had been eaten in total silence. He had his wife there for one purpose, and it seemed that although he had ordered her to be with him at meal times, he did not in fact have the slightest interest in her.

One day when they had been married just over a week, he asked what she did with her time during the day, and Sarah was able to answer truthfully that each morning after breakfast she walked into the hills behind the villa, and that she had found some antiquities in a field.

'You are interested in such things?' he asked, but casually.

'Yes, I am. I'm wondering why you don't call in the archaeologists.'

'I might, one day,' he answered, surprising her. 'This island was once one of the most sacred places in ancient Greece. The antiquities you saw are the remains of a temple to Apollo, but there are other temples, one to Zeus and one to his wife, Hera.'

'It's all very interesting. I'd love to watch the

archaeologists at work. I did belong to the Archaeological Society in England. It was fun, going out on Sundays and digging. . . .' She tailed off, aware that she was actually adopting a friendly attitude towards him, a circumstance that both amazed and angered her.

'What else do you do?' he wanted to know. 'Have you looked at the books in the library?'

'Yes, I've borrowed one or two.'

One evening at dinner, when the silence between them became unbearable, she broke it by asking him if he had always spent his days shut up in the one room as he was doing now.

'For the past three years I have, yes.'

'It's three years since your wife died?' she ventured, at the same time steeling herself for the stormy response she felt sure would come.

But to her surprise he merely said, 'It is, yes. When she was alive, I didn't live here.'

'Not here?'

'No. We lived in Athens.' He looked at her, a sort of glazed expression in his eyes. 'She never lived here. If she had, then I'd have burnt the place down rather than live in it myself!' His black eyes seemed to have ignited deep within their sockets; the sensuous mouth was twisted into an ugly line and the hand resting on the white table-cloth clenched so tightly that the knuckle bones seemed almost as if they would break the skin. Undoubtedly he was in the grip of some oppressive emotion, his staring eyes looking into the past. What had happened? Sarah wondered, by no means for the first time. She met her husband's eyes across the table . . . and was stunned by the little burst of pity that touched her heart.

Chapter Six

Sarah sat on the terrace and watched the mysterious afterglow of sunset spread its purple shadows across the vast dome of the heavens, obliterating the reds and yellows and fiery golds. Shadows stole over the garden, and the olives in the *perivoli* blended with the lemon trees and oranges until all became one dark, indistinct shape. The first intrepid stars pierced the canopy of velvet, glittering, blue-white, like April frost in the morning sun. Darkness fell swiftly, the miracle of sunset giving way to the drowsy softness of a Grecian night. Even the air was soft as thistledown, filled with heady garden scents diffused by the gentle breeze drifting in from the sea.

'Are you sitting in the dark?' The deep-toned foreign voice of her husband brought a frown to Sarah's eyes. She had been enjoying the peace, and his intruding presence angered her.

'I like the darkness. You can appreciate the radiance of the stars.'

'You're a strange woman, Sarah.' He lifted a hand to snap on a light.

'And you're a strange man.'

'I know it. I have reason to be strange. There was a time when I was not so strange, though.'

Sarah bit her lip. There could be no mistaking what he meant. He was referring to those days when he was a young man, kind and compassionate and loving, a man with ideals ... ideals that had been shattered, ruthlessly, by what his wife had done to him.

She felt him come close and steeled herself for his touch. It came—his hand on her hair, then on her face and the sensitive place behind her ear. And now it was curling round her throat, and with a little cry she sprang to her feet, bent on escape, but his arm came around her waist and she was brought up against his body. Her head was tilted up and she felt her lips captured even as her body was captured, and she could not fight, knowing from bitter experience that she would suffer for it. From the second night she had resolved never again to put up any resistance, but to let him have his way with her, which he would have anyway, because he meant to show her who was master, to show her the futility of resisting him. She parted her lips at the silent command of his sensuous mouth; she felt its moisture as his tongue probed the depths of her mouth. Vibrations shook her, sensations of pleasure she did not want. Hatred was all she wanted to feel for him.

'You're beginning to like my caresses.' Carl's voice was a sneer, his fingers cruel as they dug into her waist. 'Soon, you'll not be able to do without me.'

Her colour rose at the bold statement, and her husband laughed at her.

'If all this gives you pleasure,' she said quiveringly, 'then you're to be pitied.'

'What do you mean?' He leant away, eyes narrowed dangerously.

'Real pleasure derives from giving pleasure to others,' she told him. 'Only a sadist would find pleasure in inflicting pain.'

He went pale with fury, and in spite of herself Sarah felt a catch of fear in her throat.

'Take care,' he snarled. 'Keep your idealistic impressions to yourself!' He flung her from him and stalked away. Sarah, her heart throbbing so loudly that she could actually hear it, sank back into the chair, reluctantly recalling his arrogant assertion that she was beginning to like his caresses. Fury swamped her, but the spark of truth which she had tried several times to smother flared to life . . . and she was forced to admit that her husband's assertion was correct.

She *was* beginning to like his caresses . . .

Pale and a little shaken by the admission, she rose from the chair and went to their room to bathe and change. It seemed incredible that she should feel a physical desire for a man like Carl, a vicious man whom she had branded a fiend, a man without mercy. But reminiscently she was dwelling on that time, long ago, when she had thrilled to his kisses, had wanted them. But he was tender with her at that time, a gentle lover, whereas now. . . . She shuddered. How could she desire that kind of treatment? She asked herself again, self-contempt so strong within her that she could not have answered the question anyway.

It was over a fortnight since her first visit to Matthew's villa, reflected Sarah, her mind confused as she walked slowly along the sandy beach. Firstly, loath as she was to admit it, she was beginning to feel pity for her husband, and more and more she wanted to discover everything about his late wife, and the circumstances both of her death and that of the child. Secondly, a guilt complex had settled in her subconscious and she was unable to erase it. Carl had said she was to blame for what had happened to him, and indirectly she was. Moreover, she couldn't get out of her mind what sort of a man he had been when she first knew him, and she found herself wishing that he was like that now. Another thing was that no matter how much he hurt her, she was reluctant to retaliate. He had suffered enough, and although sometimes she was driven to anger by something Carl said or did, she was always careful not to go too far.

What was happening to her? She was restless, but in a different way from before, and it was as if a desire had been born that was so intangible as to be no more than the elusive thread of a dream. She often found herself looking at her husband and wanting to say something to take the brooding expression from his face. Fierce and evil he might have appeared to her at first, but now. . . . Nothing in his appearance had changed, nothing in the arrogant way he made love to her, nothing in the way he spoke. Yet she was beginning to hate him a little less.

She was glad when she reached the villa and went through the gate, closing it behind her. She was feeling the peace of her surroundings already, and she thought she would like to make Maroula's acquaintance when she returned, which would be two days after Matthew had left. Aunt and nephew were meeting in Athens and then each going their separate ways.

Matthew opened the door to her as usual and threw it wide for her to enter. He smiled and said he would bring the coffee out to the patio. Sarah sat down, relaxing against the back of the chair. She could see the mountains over the tops of the trees, their summits bruised by wind and rain, their colour dove-grey as clouds shaded them from the sun. To the east, where a golden sheen still persisted, the hills glowed orange and peach-saffron, while to the west a mist was pressing on the horizon so that it faded into the sky in a flurry of purple and blue-brown.

So much variety in the far distance, while at hand the glorious riot of colour and heady perfume as a myriad exotic flowers lifted their faces to the sun.

Matthew returned, placing her coffee on the table in front of her. He was good-looking, she thought, wondering why she had not noticed before. She saw his eyes fall to her left hand, where the plain gold band caught the sun, a thick band with no accompanying engagement ring. Was it regret she saw in his eyes?

'What have you been doing with yourself besides reading?' she asked, speaking into the silence. 'Have you been doing any gardening?'

'A little. After that violent thunder-storm we had the other day, the weeds sprang up overnight! I had to clear them before they had the chance to grow and become more difficult to get up.'

'Aren't you finding it a bit lonely here?' She was speaking for something to say, half-wishing it was time for him to leave, so that he could take her letter.

'It's exceptionally quiet,' he admitted ruefully. 'I hadn't expected my aunt's villa to be quite so far from other habitation. Still, she likes it, and that's all that matters.' Leaning forward, he picked up his coffee cup. 'And what have you been doing with yourself?' he asked, regarding her curiously.

She shrugged airily. 'Oh, having a nice, quiet time,' she replied.

'You're still on your honeymoon, of course.'

'Yes, that's right.'

'You didn't want to go away?'

'No—my husband's rather busy. He spends a lot of his time in his study.'

'Leaving you to amuse yourself?'

'I don't find it difficult,' she lied.

'It seems a strange sort of honeymoon to me . . .' He broke off, a flush rising beneath the clear light skin of his face. 'Sorry. That just slipped out. Sorry,' he added again, and got up to fetch more coffee.

He seemed to be a long time gone, and when he returned she said it was time she was leaving.

'I've upset you, haven't I?' he murmured with regret. 'I don't often speak out of turn.'

'You've not upset me,' she assured him. 'But I must go. I can't have my husband waiting for me. We have breakfast at about a quarter to nine.' She rose as she spoke, and he asked when she would be along again.

'I don't know. . . . Perhaps in two or three days' time.'

'Don't forget to come for coffee, will you?'

She smiled, feeling sorry for him because he was obviously beginning to feel lonely.

'No, I won't forget,' she promised, and with a wave of the hand, she left him.

Over lunch that day Carl asked Sarah to go to the village for him.

'I want a few things from the chemist's,' he added. 'I've made a list.'

She actually gave him a smile, feeling happy at the thought of doing something for him. She took the list and went off, her mind in a whirl of conflicting thoughts. How could this change be coming over her? She had been taken prisoner, forced into marriage with a man she had hated; she would be kept here until she produced the child he wanted from her, and then she would be freed—cast off, in fact. All this, and yet she could be happy at the idea of doing a service for him. It was incredible!

She had to walk along the waterfront to get to the village, and she could not help but notice the covert, interested stares that came her way as she passed, first, fishermen chatting and spreading their nets for drying, then the men sprawled in front of the *taverna*, drinking ouzo and playing *tavli*. Their dark eyes followed her slender figure—stripping it, she did not doubt, because she knew from her previous visits to Athens that all Greek men were like that. Why, if they were so fond of looking at the female figure, didn't they bring their wives out? But no; Greek wives, like so many women from the East, spent most of their lifetime either slaving in the home or in the fields. Beasts of burden, no more, no less.

The chemist's was right on the corner, run by a tall, angular Greek with a heavy crop of greying hair and a thin, lined face.

'*Yassoo!*' he greeted her. '*Kyria* Carlos. Welcome to our island.' He bowed slightly, surprising her, as Greeks did not usually extend this kind of courtesy to women. It must be because she was the wife of the island's owner, she accepted, as the thought struck her. 'What can I do for you?'

'I have a list here.' She passed it over to him and five minutes later was walking out with the parcel in her hand. She was sauntering along, looking in the various shop windows, when, on impulse, she went into the wool shop, which, she saw, sold embroidery materials. She would embroider a cushion cover or something. It would help to relieve the monotony of her day.

The shop was dark and smelled of must. Whoever
was supposed to be attending to it was in a small room
at the back, talking to someone, loudly, as all Greek
women do. Sarah tapped lightly on the counter and
received no response. She was just about to tap again
when she stiffened on hearing her husband's name,
and within seconds she realised that the two women
were having a conversation about her husband's hasty
marriage, and they were speaking in English, though
very broken. However, Sarah was able to understand
most of what they were saying. She had already
guessed that gossip would be rife, and that the shops
in the village would be the centre of such gossip.

'Yannis was in here this morning and he said that
Mr Carlos eats and sleeps with her and that is all.'

'It is very funny, *ochi!'*

'Yannis was working for Mr Carlos in Athens, when
his other wife was living. He say that there always
trouble and Mr Carlos haf life of hell!'

'You mean, they haf many quarrels?'

'Yannis say so. Mr Carlos' woman haf many pillow
friends; she very bad person, but Mr Carlos not know
this when he marry her.'

'Yannis would be in trouble if Mr Carlos know he
come here and talk. What is eet he want to buy?'

'Some needles and cotton.' A pause followed, and
Sarah, every nerve tensed, waited impatiently for
more information about her husband's past life. 'Mr
Carlos' wife not like the way Mr Carlos love child, so
she . . .' The voice trailed away to silence, and Sarah,
aware that at least one of the women had realised
there was a customer waiting, turned swiftly and left
the shop, frustrated at not hearing any more.

Carl's wife had obviously resented her husband's

love for the child and had. . . . What? A shiver passed along Sarah's spine. It couldn't be murder!

She hurried on, feeling icy cold. What, she wondered, would Carl think if he were to know that his servant Yannis had been into the village gossiping about him. That he would be furious went without saying. He would most certainly dismiss the man as well.

On arriving back at the villa, she put the parcel on the table in the hall, her eyes wandering to the door at the far end. Carl's study . . . and the door always closed. She had never been inside, never even glimpsed it from the outside. He had his business to look after, but somehow Sarah could not accept that it took all the time he was in there. Rather did she suspect that he sat there brooding over his past hurts.

She went out to the garden, restlessly wandering about, until, finally, she decided to take a walk along the beach. As she neared Matthew's villa, she glanced into the garden. No sign of Matthew, and she concluded that he must be on the patio at the back, reading. She walked on, towards the rocky cliff, with the intention of looking for the way across it mentioned by Matthew. She found it quite easily and threaded her precarious way over the loose boulders, which, hammered and pounded by the sea over countless ages, were smooth and shiny—and dangerous. But she managed to negotiate them with a fair amount of ease, and when she saw the view from the other side, she decided it had been well worth the trouble. She stood staring across the sunlit sea, when a movement caught her eye and with a little exclamation of astonishment she saw her husband swimming strongly in the water. He was a long way from the shore, but she stepped back, out of his full view, her eyes narrowed against the brittle glare of the sun, focusing on his body, and even at this distance she could sense the magnificent power of his limbs. He was coming in, and as he drew nearer she noticed the slim and muscular lines of his body as he moved with the effortless ease and grace of a creature born to the marine depths. An inexplicable stirring of emotion brought an increase of her heartbeats; she admitted with a little access of shock that she would have liked nothing better than to be out there with him, their bodies close, part of the ceaseless motion of the sea.

For a few moments longer she watched him as he made for the rocky part of the shore. Memory drifted to her on gentle wings . . . and she was hearing a handsome young Greek saying he would make love to her in romantic places, like in the water where the rocks would hide them. . . .

She drew a long breath, aware of sensations pleasant and yet vague, of her pulse starting to race, and of a yearning which in itself was a sense of loss.

She moved a little, effectively concealing herself behind jutting rocks, her eyes still following him as he swam towards the shore, then came out of the water. He stood for a moment, his toughly sinewed body tall and straight and darkly bronzed, glistening in the sunlight. She quivered involuntarily as her eyes fluttered over the whole length of him, and she coloured. She had known his body, suffered from its muscular hardness, had even clung to it more than once when, with pagan determination and mastery, he had compelled her to respond to his love-making; but not until now had she seen it properly. He picked up a towel he had hung on a rock, and her eyes followed the movements of his lean brown hands as he used the towel to dry himself. Her breath caught; she was vitally aware of him as a man, deeply conscious of his great strength and magnetic personality as he stood there, aloof as a Greek god, his harsh, arrogant face turned towards the sun.

Having finished with the towel, he slung it over his shoulder, and Sarah realised that now was the time to move, swiftly, so that she could find shelter in the bushes behind the shore, for she had no wish that he should know she frequented this part of the beach.

And that her action had been prudent was proved the following morning. She had strolled only part way towards Matthew's villa, and decided to turn back. To her surprise, Carl was on the front terrace, and he asked her where she had been.

'Walking on the beach,' she answered, and saw a slight narrowing of his eyes.

'Are you in the habit of walking on the beach?'

'Yes, I walk along it every morning.'

'Which way do you go?' He seemed anxious, she thought, as he waited for her reply.

'Sometimes I turn left and sometimes right.'

'Have you ever met anyone?' he queried slowly, his eyes boring into the depths of hers.

'Met anyone, at this time of the morning?' she rejoined, feigning surprise.

'You've not met Maroula?'

She shook her head, relieved that she could answer him truthfully.

'No, I haven't met anyone by that name. Does she go for morning walks along the shore?' she decided to add, just for effect.

He made no immediate answer. He seemed thoughtful, and her heart missed a beat. It was obvious that he had no idea that Maroula was away, that her nephew was in her house; it was also obvious that he was afraid of Sarah's meeting and making friends with the woman.

A long tense silence ensued before he said, 'Watch yourself, Sarah. If I have the least inkling that you are seeking help to get away from this island, I shall not hesitate to lock you up. Understand?'

'Yes, Carl,' she said, marvelling at her ability to look him straight in the eye when she was planning to send a letter to Avril. 'Yes, I understand perfectly.'

Chapter Seven

Sarah strolled along the beach towards Matthew's villa. He was leaving on the afternoon ferry, and she had not yet mentioned the letter she wanted him to post. It had taken her over an hour to write it, as she had scrapped several sheets of paper before being able to produce anything that remotely satisfied her. The whole episode of her being left by Eric and forced into marriage seemed ludicrous when set down on paper. Finally, however, she had managed to write what seemed moderately feasible, and the urgency of the ending should make Avril realise the terrible plight her sister was in.

'For God's sake don't waste any time, Avril—I must get away from here! Get in touch with the police at Rhodes immediately and repeat everything that I have written.'

'Hello,' Matthew greeted her as she reached the

gate where he was waiting, a smile on his lips. 'Another beautiful morning! I shall miss this place— although,' he added with a grimace, 'it's beginning to pall—the loneliness, I mean.'

She followed him through the living-room to the patio, where he left her while he went off to make the coffee.

At first she had had some trouble in trying to devise a way of asking him to post the letter without his being puzzled. Then a very simple way had come to her, and she spoke immediately upon his return with the coffee.

'I wonder if you'd post a letter for me when you get to London, Matthew?' She flashed him her brightest smile. 'It's to my sister, and if it's posted here it has to go first to Rhodes, then Athens, then London; it could take ten days or more—'

'I know it,' he broke in. 'Letters sent to me by my aunt often take that long.'

'Well, as it does happen to be rather urgent, I'd be very grateful if you'd post it in London.' Her heart was beating swiftly. She seemed so much nearer freedom already. 'I've got it with me because I was sure you'd do the favour for me.' Taking it from her pocket, she placed it on the table. Matthew picked it up, scanned the envelope, and said, 'This is only about two miles from where I live. It's a small world.'

They chatted for a little while, and then Sarah rose to leave.

'It was nice knowing you,' he said as they stood by the gate. 'I'll be telling Aunt Maroula about you when I meet her in Athens tomorrow. You must come along and see her, Sarah. You'll like her; she's very English in her ways, and speaks the language perfectly.' He stopped, his glance moving from Sarah's lovely face to her shining hair and then back again to look deeply into her eyes. 'It's been nice knowing you, Sarah,' he said again. 'And I shall be back perhaps next year—I hope.' Before she could guess at his intention, he had leant over the gate to kiss her on the cheek. 'Take care of yourself,' he said. 'I shall be asking Aunt Maroula about you in my letters.'

She fluttered him a smile, feeling sad at the idea of his leaving, and yet, paradoxically, she would have helped him on his way if she could, so eager was she to get the letter to Avril.

That afternoon she stood high on a hill and watched the ferry sail away from the little harbour, carrying Matthew . . . and her letter. She was filled with exultation at being able to thwart her husband. What a shock he would receive when the police from Rhodes came to see him! She would make sure she herself met them first, to give them the full story. They would then see Carl and she would be freed, insisting they take her with them back to Rhodes.

'I've won!' she cried, still keeping the ferry in sight even though it was becoming lost in the quivering blue haze that was descending over the sea. 'In less than a week I could be free!'

Excitement affected every nerve in her body. Freedom had been impossible until she met Matthew three weeks ago. It seemed like a miracle that he should come to Comaris for a holiday and so make it possible for her even to consider escaping from her husband's clutches. Certainly fate had played into her hands on that morning when she heard Matthew's cheery greeting, and the idea of using him as her messenger had been born.

She was so high-spirited that it was inevitable that Carl should notice. Her eyes were brighter than they had been for a month, her cheeks flushed, and even the way she carried herself, and the way she walked, with a much lighter step than before—all these were different.

'You're brighter these days,' he said, unable to prevent his searching glance from exploring her figure. 'Can it be that my child is on the way?'

'No—!' She coloured painfully, 'I don't want your child!'

'But,' he reminded her softly, 'you'll not be free until you've had my child—till you've had a son,' he added significantly.

She moistened her lips, forgetting for a moment that freedom was close, and thinking instead what it would be like if she had a daughter, then another . . . and another. She shivered, as a sudden chill brought ice to her blood. But that was not going to happen! She would be away from here before this time next week! He could then find some other woman to present him with the son he wanted!

As the days passed she was mentally following Matthew's movements. The boat trip to Rhodes, then the flight to Athens, where he would meet his aunt. They were having dinner together and staying the night in the city before parting, each to return to his own home. Then Matthew would fly to London, where he would post her letter. It should not take more than a day to reach her sister, but even allowing two days, she should receive it by Thursday. She would get in touch with the Rhodes police without delay, and in turn they would come speeding out to Comaris to rescue her. In all, estimated Sarah, it should not take more than four or five days at the very outside before the arrival of the Greek police, who, she was sure, would not wait for the sailing day of Carl's ferry, but would use their own launch.

With every passing day her excitement grew, and by the fourth day she awoke feeling actually light-headed, as if she were flying away from her captor already.

What a stir it would cause on the island! The noble owner visited by the police, and his wife taken away from him. Suddenly Sarah was frowning, biting her lip as her mind created a picture of her husband being interviewed by the police, of him sitting there listening to her accusations against him, of his final chagrin and humiliation when she went away with the police. . . .

Already she had told herself that he had suffered enough, and had resolved not to hurt him. She had kept to her resolve, puzzling Carl at times by her lack of retaliation when he said things which, in the beginning, would very quickly have aroused her anger.

What of her resolve now—when she was praying for the arrival of the police from Rhodes? What was the matter with her, she was asking herself. Why should she care about Carl's feelings in this way? Why should it trouble her whenever she thought of his being hurt? Inevitably she recalled those moments when she had been so vitally moved by the sight of him, moved in a way she could not understand . . . or could it be that she did not want to understand? Was she shirking, straining with everything in her to annihilate the incipient question that hovered somewhere in the recesses of her mind—crushing it because the answer might appall her?

It was with considerable difficulty that she managed to throw off her qualms. She wanted her freedom, and that must be the factor that would influence her every thought and action. She was sorry for her husband, but she was also sorry for herself. She had not asked for the treatment he had meted out to her. True, she had turned down his proposal of marriage, but that was her own affair. She had not wanted to marry either him or anyone else, and he should have accepted her refusal with more understanding. There was of course the matter of her marriage to Arthur Grimsby—and she had already made excuses for Carl's hatred of her. He was a Greek, and not used to being humiliated by a woman, but nevertheless, she would not think of him, but of herself. And with this resolution firmly fixed in her mind she waited expectantly for the arrival of the police.

But the days went by and nothing happened. Then a week, and another, until Sarah tearfully reached the conclusion that Matthew had forgotten to post her letter. Meanwhile, she had gone along to the little villa with the intention of making herself known to Maroula, but to her disappointment, she was not there. When a second visit produced no result either, Sarah concluded that Maroula must be having a prolonged holiday in Athens. But when a third visit proved equally abortive, she did not know what to think. In any case, there was nothing she could do except keep repeating her visits until she did find Maroula in.

'You're restless again,' her husband complained one

day when she had been wandering aimlessly about the garden. 'I've been watching you through the window of my study,' he added, his dark eyes frowning as they searched her face. 'What's the matter with you?'

'You can ask that?' She stared at him in amazement. 'I'm a prisoner, kept like some prize animal who's supposed to produce something rather special! You have the nerve to ask me what's wrong?' She turned away, but his hand shot out to halt her, and she was jerked around again.

'I complained about your turn of phrase before,' he snarled. 'Guard your tongue if you don't want to smart!' And with that he swung away, fury in every step he took as he made his way towards the open French window of his study. Sarah, nerves on edge, and more depressed than before, almost ran from the garden towards the gate which led to the narrow tree-lined road along which she and Eric had come on that first fateful day. It led down to the village and the harbour, but she took the opposite direction and within ten minutes she had left the road and was making her way through a quiet woodland glade which she had visited only once before. It was on the edge of this glade that she had found the antiquities—some columns almost buried by loess and the vegetation that had taken a foothold upon it. Now she went on, tears running down her face, her mind obsessed by misery. What had happened to her letter? If Matthew had lost it, he would probably let his aunt know, but his aunt had not returned. Everything was against her, it seemed. She trudged on and on, uncaring that her steps were taking her deeper and deeper into what was now a thick forest of trees. The ground flattened out, and she was on a plateau which, if it had not been partly covered by trees, would have commanded a magnificent view in every direction except to the north, where the highest mountains were, the summit of Mount Ayios Elias rising slightly above other, equally magnificent peaks. A marvellous site for a villa, she thought, desperately trying to keep her mind from dwelling on her wretched situation. She sat down on the trunk of a dead tree, cupping her chin in her hands and staring into space. From the trees the incessant whirring of cicadas intruded into her quiet thoughts, while intruding into her vision came a giant green lizard, to stop and remain motionless before disappearing beneath a rock. A rock . . . ? Sarah's eyes flickered, then widened, and she got up to investigate. A piece of stone with carving on it! She began scraping away with her hands, dragging vegetation out by the roots. She found nothing, but was convinced that she was on a site where antiquities could be found. Why didn't Carl call in the archaeologists? There might be marvellous treasures hidden beneath the lush green cover of parts of this island. She stood looking around; everything seemed to be wrapped in a kind of primordial silence, for suddenly even the cicadas were no longer to be heard. Her eyes continued to scan the whole area.

Rising behind the plateau was a hill, partly wooded with olives and limes and plane trees. Her wandering eyes were suddenly stilled, their attention caught by a strange feature on the hillside that could not possibly be natural. She knew a little about geomorphology— the formation of the land through the forces of nature; mainly wind, water and ice. This was no natural feature created by those forces. . . . Her slight knowl-

edge of archaeology included a little about chamber
tombs, underground burial chambers, usually cut into
the side of a hill.

Moving towards the feature, she stood examining
the whole area around it. Yes, definitely not anything
sculptured by nature . . . but by man, thousands of
years ago. And somewhere there must be an entrance,
with a passage leading to it . . .

She began to pull away at the vegetation, but it soon
daunted her, as the roots went very deep into the
earth, tangling themselves up with other roots.

The sun was going down when at last she decided
to leave, but she made sure she could find her way
back, which she intended to do tomorrow, and she
would bring some tools with her.

To her surprise, Carl was in the garden when she
got back, and she watched him for a space as he stood
staring down at a bed of beautiful crimson roses. He
stooped, picked one, put it between his teeth and
walked away.

'A rose . . .' There was something profoundly moving about a man like Carl with a rose in his mouth.
. . . Sarah found herself swallowing hard, trying to
dislodge the little ache that had suddenly caught her
throat.

At the dinner table that evening he was rather more
talkative than usual. He seemed to have taken a little
more trouble over his appearance, too, she realised on
noticing the pale mauve shirt with a small black-
edged frill down the front, and the perfection of the
black bow-tie. Sarah was dressed in a long skirt which
Theodora had brought up for her to see a few days
ago. It was bright red, and apart from the hand-
embroidered trimming on the hem, it was simplicity

itself, merely being gathered into a waistband which fastened at the back with ties of the same material. With it she wore a plain white blouse with high mandarin collar. The sleeves were long and full, gathered into tight cuffs fastened with small pearl buttons. Carl looked her over as she entered the room, an odd expression crossing his face before it set into an inscrutable mask.

'You look very charming,' he said, surprising her, but his voice was as expressionless as his face. He drew out her chair for her, something he had not troubled to do before. And she was sure she felt his chin touch her hair . . .

Androula had put candles on the table, and two small flower arrangements, one at each end. Petros came in with soup, as usual serving Carl first. But with a flick of the hand and a curt, 'Serve Mrs Carlos first,' Carl again surprised his wife. She did not know what to make of him, but if he noticed her puzzlement, he refrained from commenting on it.

'Have you got over your doldrums of this afternoon?' he said, picking up his spoon.

'I feel better, yes.' Her thoughts strayed to the find she believed she had made on that lonely hillside, far away from the village or habitation of any kind. The land belonged to Carl, so there was no one likely to object if she went there again and began to investigate. It would give her something to do, for otherwise she felt she would go mad.

'You went somewhere?'

'I walked, into the woods. It was peaceful.' She toyed with the croutons floating on her soup. 'It was something to do.'

'You're bored?'

'Naturally I'm bored. It's superfluous for you to ask a question like that.'

The black eyes glittered threateningly. 'Be careful. I've warned you more than once to treat me with respect.'

She began to eat her soup, keeping her temper, even though it strained at the bonds.

'Which woods were you walking in?' asked Carl after a pause.

'They're over there.' She flipped a hand towards the east window, indicating an opposite direction to that where she had been. She had no intention of telling him of her find, not only because she might be wrong, and it was not a grave at all, but also because she felt sure he would be awkward and forbid her to investigate.

'The ground's swampy,' he warned. 'Watch yourself. I'm surprised you haven't noticed.'

His glance was questioning, and Sarah replied swiftly, 'Perhaps I hadn't gone in deep enough.'

'Well, take care if you go there again.'

Petros came in to take away the soup dishes, while Yannis uncorked the wine, poured it, and returned the bottle to the cooler.

'Don't you ever go for walks?' she asked, the picture of him swimming in the sea vivid in her mind.

'Sometimes. I don't have much time.' He had picked up his glass and was idly watching the bubbles rising through the pale amber of the wine.

'What do you do all day?' she asked, encouraged by this change in him. 'Aren't you bored, in your study, by yourself all the time?'

'I find something to occupy my mind.'

'But everyone needs recreation.' She scarcely knew

that her voice was persuasive; she did know that, deep within her, she was troubled about him. He was so lonely, so isolated from everything and everyone, including his wife.

'I've no desire for recreation.' He seemed tired, she thought, and dejected.

'But exercise, Carl—you must have exercise . . .' Sarah's voice trailed as she noticed his expression.

'Anyone would think that my wife is anxious about me,' he remarked with a hint of mockery. She said nothing, and after a moment he added, 'If it's so important that I have exercise, then you shall accompany me on a stroll later, when we've finished dinner.'

The beach was deserted as usual. Sarah and Carl walked in the opposite direction from that which she usually took. The night was silent, drenched in moonlight, the sea like glass coated with silver, the mountains spangled with stardust. Sarah, caught in a web of witchery spun by the magic around her, knew a sense of unreality, feeling herself suspended in isolation where only the tall gaunt man beside her seemed real as they walked, side by side, along the sands, the air fragrant with the scent of herbs flourishing among the undergrowth that inhabited the backshore. Carl stopped, to stare at a liner flaunting its lights on the horizon. She saw his face in profile, the lines harsh in the moonlight, his broad shoulders drooping a little. His mouth was taut, the lips compressed, and she swallowed as she remembered just how cruel they could be. He turned, as if drawn by her intense stare, and while her face was uplifted, he bent his head and kissed her on the lips. So gentle . . . and the arms that came about her were almost tender. A great shuddering sigh rose from the depths of him as he held her, close to his heart, his chin resting on the top of her head.

'Carl . . .' It was a strangled little whisper that escaped from her lips. 'I . . . you . . .'

Did he smile? Impossible to tell, but it did seem that there was a fleeting flash of strong white teeth before his lips claimed hers again. It began as a gentle kiss, but within seconds his ardour flamed and Sarah knew again the fiery passion of his Greek nature, the crushing dominance of his lips, the bruising strength of his arms. Her heart pounded, its wild pulsations affecting every nerve in her body. His hands caressed, one finding the fastener at the back of her skirt. And as she felt his hand slide down, between the soft cotton of the skirt and the filmy material of her underskirt, every inch of her body was ignited by the conflagration of his ardour. She swayed close in erotic accord to the persuasion of a hand crushing her breast, then responded, the hungry torment of her own desire conveyed to him as she arched her supple body, her soft breath against his face a whispered moan of ecstasy.

'How easy it's becoming to bring you to the state of surrender.' His low mocking laugh brought colour flooding to her face, and she knew he was aware of it although he could not see it. Pushing her hand against his chest, she freed herself and turned away.

'I hate you,' she whispered fervently. 'Hate you, do you hear?'

'I hear but I don't heed.' Again the mocking note, but in the timbre of his voice this time. 'Why don't I heed, Sarah? Because you lie. There was no hate in the kisses you gave me just now.'

'What are you trying to say?' She swung around

again, her voice quivering with fury born of the
knowledge that he spoke the truth.

'I'll not say it,' he returned, 'because you know it,
don't you? Just as I do.'

Something within her snapped. She had tried to
control herself, but at his present manner fury erupt-
ed and resolve went by the board.

'Yes,' she flashed, 'yes, we do know, don't we?
—know that I pity you! Yes, I pity you with all my
heart!—just as I would pity anyone as wicked as you,
for it's a disease you have—the result of genetics!
Pity—you need it—'

'Shut up!' With a gesture of unbridled wrath he
seized her by the shoulders and shook her violently.
'Pity!' he spat out, his breath fanning her face. 'Don't
you dare say I need pity! It's you who need pity—and
you'll need it more before I've finished with you!' He
pushed her from him, but aware that she was about to
fall, he retained a hold on her arms.

'I do pity myself,' she assured him, her voice
breaking and her eyes misty with tears. 'I pity us
both—two people being crucified while fate looks on
and laughs!' Sarah's own laugh cracked hysterically.
'And who caused it all? *She* did—your wife—a woman
who is dead and still exerting her influence on the
living. Well, she can influence you for the rest of your
life, but she'll not influence me! I shall . . . shall . . .'
She tailed off, because her husband had brought her
to him, and because she could never have finished a
sentence she did not mean, and because she needed
the comfort Carl was giving her. She wept unrestrain-
edly against his breast, while her hand stole up to his
shoulder in a childish, involuntary gesture.

'Sarah,' he murmured, his lips on her temple, 'don't
cry like that—don't cry, I say!'

They walked slowly back to the house, Sarah's body still quivering from the aftermath of the weeping. She went to their bedroom immediately and flung herself down on the bed, using every ounce of determination in her to regain control of her emotions. Shaken to the depths as Carl knew she was, she had hoped he would not come to her, and indeed she convinced herself that he would not come. She undressed, slipping into a nightgown and then a négligé. Desperate for the cool silence and solitude that the verandah would provide, she opened the window and stepped out, lifting her face to catch the last of the dying Etesian wind drifting in from the sea. She had been there for ten minutes or so when, with a sinking heart, she heard her husband in the room behind. For a long while she remained where she was, hoping for a miracle. But she realised that he had no intention of leaving when she heard the firm command in his voice as he said, 'Come here, Sarah.'

Resignedly she turned; she had neither the strength nor the will to defy him. And slowly she entered the room, moving towards where he stood, by the bed.

'I'm tired,' she faltered, and shook her head as if to remind herself that she wasted her words.

'I'm your husband, Sarah, and it so happens that I desire you tonight. I was bound to, wasn't I, with the preliminaries we went through outside?'

'Don't,' she begged. 'There's no need to be crude about it, Carl.' She moved to the bed, slipped off the négligé and lay down, pulling the covers up, but only to her waist.

He looked at her perceptively. 'You believe your attitude will put me off?' A sneer caught his mouth, lifting one corner. 'Alas for your hopes, my dear. Your little stratagem is wasted.' He spoke with all the familiar arrogance and mastery in his harsh and foreign voice, and yet Sarah sensed a regret, a hint of apology somewhere in its depths, and she realised that his need of her was greater than the chivalry he might otherwise have extended to her.

She felt his naked body beside her, his hands caressing, stimulating her desire in spite of her depressed state of mind. She knew a wild leaping of her pulses, a craving for fulfillment. A husky little sound escaped her as she melted under the fierce flame of his ardour.

Chapter Eight

There was a brooding expression on Sarah's face as she sat on the sunlit patio, her eyes following her husband's movements in the water.

She had not been invited to be here; she had just happened to come along, unaware that he was swimming, in the peace and tranquillity of the delightful setting in which the pool was located. Trees—palms and jacarandas—rose as a backdrop to the flaring hibiscus hedge on one side, a bank of pink and white oleanders on another, while at each narrower end were masses of exotic flowers growing in ornamental urns and earthenware pots of local manufacture.

Carl had seen her arrive, only to stop suddenly, in the manner of someone who realises she was trespassing.

'There's no need to go,' he had assured her as she turned away. And she fluttered him a smile then, and stayed by the pool for a space, looking down at him before, with a feeling of pleasure, she sat down on one of the chairs.

And now she could not take her eyes off him; he seemed to fascinate her, to draw her irresistibly, like a moth to a flame. Tinglings indescribable . . . tremors along her spine and delicious pulsations in the region of her heart. . . . Was this the beginning of love? She had never even contemplated being in love, her attitude being what it was regarding marriage. Not for her the pain and disillusionment suffered by others, or the feeling of inadequacy bred by the knowledge that her man had left her for someone else—she, whom he had once loved and cherished and for whom he had promised to forsake all others. All else being equal, though, the woman fared far worse than the man in marriage. It had always seemed to Sarah that the woman did most of the giving, the man most of the receiving, and she had wanted no part of it.

But now. . . . She hated the admission that she was beginning to care, simply because he was not the kind of man any self-respecting woman would fall in love with. But into her mind would come the picture—so very clear—of what Carl used to be. Handsome and noble of feature, with a superlative physique and a happy, loving nature. A man of forceful personality and quiet strength and yet kind and gentle and compassionate. A happy young man as yet untouched by the hurts that a ruthless fate was to inflict upon him.

He looked up and smiled; she felt the quickening of an altogether new emotion, which could not by any stretch of imagination be regarded as pity. Ought she to be shocked by these truths? Where would love for a man like Carl lead her? To slavery and destruction! Yes, she was sure of it! 'I must get away,' she whispered. 'It's even more urgent now than before . . . because to love him would be crucifying.'

She eased herself up from the chair and he said, 'Are you going?' just as if he wanted her to stay.

Warmth spread over her even though she tried to remain immune to anything remotely persuasive on his part.

'I . . . er . . . I was going, yes.'

'Where are you going?' he wanted to know. He was coming out, and she watched him spring himself up onto the side of the pool and sit on the green, carpet-like material that went all round the pool-patio. Above him a tamarisk tree allowed only filters of sun to penetrate and, caught in these quivering rays, his face seemed softer, more human. Sarah lowered her lashes, hiding her expression from eyes that were subjecting her to a most intense and searching scrutiny.

'I was going for a stroll,' she answered. 'There's time before lunch.'

He was towelling himself and she watched his movements as she had watched him once before. He had no inhibitions, she noticed, a tinge of colour fusing her cheeks. Her eyes lifted, covertly; he caught her glance and she saw the hint of mocking amusement that crossed his face, fleetingly, and then it was gone. It reminded her, somehow, of what he had been. And yet he never once mocked in those days. He loved her too much, adored and worshiped her. She had been his ideal, and he had put her on a pedestal.

She tried to visualise what he would have been like now, seven years on, if life had been good to him, inflicting no scars.

And she suddenly found that her cheeks were wet . . .

'I'm . . . I'm going for that walk,' she said hastily. 'I need the exercise.'

He shrugged, tossing the towel aside. And when she looked around as she was crossing the garden, she saw that he had gone back into the water.

The hillside looked so ordinary, mused Sarah as she approached it across the forested plateau. To the unsuspecting eye it was just a hill, like any other hill, but to her . . . She could be wrong, but she rather thought she was right. A tomb, burial chamber of some family? Of course, a *tholos* tomb could be there, but Sarah was doubtful, since *tholos* tombs were usually for royalty, and she did not think that a king would live here, on this comparatively small island, though one never knew.

How to begin? She would dearly have loved to confide in Carl and ask him to get help from the experts. Perhaps she would ask him later, but not until she could be sure there really was a tomb under that strange-looking feature on the side of the hill. She swung around on her heels, regarding other hills, distant ones, and wondering if their lime and olive trees sheltered treasures unexplored. Most tombs had been robbed at some time in antiquity, but some remained. And of those robbed, many still contained some treasures, the robbers evidently having found some difficulty in disposing of the things they had already stolen.

She had managed to get a short-handled implement

from one of the garden sheds at the back of the villa. It was rather like a spade but its blade came to a point. Her only other tool was similar to a pick, but with shorter prongs and shaft. Not much to tackle a job of that magnitude, she thought ruefully. Nevertheless, she intended to have a good search for the entrance.

She had been trying to remember what she had learned about chamber tombs in the lectures she used to attend at the university, and although much of it came back, a good deal eluded her. However, if she could find any sign of an entrance, then she would have the proof she needed to get her husband interested. It did not strike her as strange that she should want to enlist his help. It seemed the natural thing to do. Of course, he might not be interested, might be averse to having not only the archaeologists brought from Athens but also the labourers needed to do the preliminary work of clearing away the tons of earth which, down through three thousand years or more, had accumulated, completely burying the tomb and the trench leading to its entrance.

Sarah worked as best she could, going every day, both before lunch and afterwards. And at last, after a full fortnight's work, she found traces of a *dromos*, which was the passage leading to the entrance. Farther along would be the burial chamber.

She was just coming away when her heart gave a great lurch and she swung round to see two dark stocky Greek youths who appeared to have been standing there for some time, watching her as she picked up some branches with which to cover the scar she had made in the hillside. She had no wish that anyone should come up here and notice that the ground had been tampered with.

'Who . . . who are you?' she faltered, every nerve

tensed. She would stand little chance of escape if these two strong-looking young men decided to attack her. 'Where did you come from?' Could they speak English? she wondered, fear parching her throat so that she found herself swallowing over and over again.

'We're from Athens,' one said in excellent English, and smiled. 'We have our mother here and we come for vacation. This is my brother, Panos, and I am Nico.' His glance went to the scar and he added, 'What are you doing?'

She sagged with relief at his words and answered truthfully, because there was nothing else she could do, 'I think I've found a chamber tomb—'

'A chamber tomb!' broke in Panos excitedly. 'I told you, Nico, that this island was important in Mycenaean times. I have been doing a lot of work on the Mycenaean civilisation and I believe that several of these islands were occupied by them,' he added, turning to Sarah.

'So you are interested in archaeology?' she asked, her eyes flickering from the face of one youth to the other, automatically searching for a likeness.

Both youths laughed.

'We are students of archaeology at the University of Athens,' Nico informed her. 'This will be wonderful if you have found a grave. You are obviously an archaeologist. But how did you come to be here, on our island? Are you visiting some friends, perhaps?'

She shook her head, hesitating, but not for long. 'I'm married to Mr Duris, and—'

'Ah! The English lady our mother spoke about! It is a pleasure for us to meet you. You have not been married for long, our mother said?'

'No,' she answered, attempting to adopt the sort of

reserved manner that would be expected of the wife of the island's owner. 'Only a few weeks, in fact.'

'This is a very great surprise, Mrs Carlos. It was not thought that Mr Carlos would marry.'

How much did these two know about her husband's past, wondered Sarah, deciding after a moment to ask the brief and leading question, 'Why?'

'Why? Er . . . well, he . . . he . . .' Panos tailed off, looking at his brother as if for advice.

'It is nothing, Mrs Carlos.' Nico smiled, his dark eyes roving her figure, taking in every delightful curve and line. 'It was such a surprise, you see. But we are very happy that he is married, and to a pretty English lady. Welcome—and we hope you will be very happy on our island.'

'Thank you, Nico.'

'About this grave,' interposed Panos eagerly, moving towards the place where Sarah had been working. 'You've been digging, all by yourself?'

She nodded and said swiftly, in order to forestall any awkward questions they might be tempted to ask, 'I wanted to make absolutely sure that there was a grave before I mentioned anything to my husband. I would have looked foolish, you see, if there hadn't been anything there at all. I am not an archaeologist, as you have assumed, but I do know a little about the subject. I used to belong to the Society in England and of course went on small digs at the week-ends, just for the excitement of it. Anyone can join the Society and take part in digs. I spent one or two of my vacations on digs—one was a Roman amphitheatre; they wanted all the students they could get.'

Panos was nodding, obviously interested in what she was saying, but equally interested in his occupation of removing more of the branches with which

Sarah had begun to cover the traces of the passage she had discovered.

'Without students, who give their time free,' he said, 'a great many archaeological sites would have to wait a long time for excavation. Students' work in the field is acknowledged to be invaluable.' Panos spoke over his shoulder, being deeply engrossed now as he began to scrape away at the earth with the spade which he had found conveniently at hand. His brother was probing with his hands at a spot nearby. 'I think you've uncovered traces of a *dromos!*' said Panos excitedly.

'The passageway?' Nico went swiftly to where his brother was standing. 'It could be . . .' He was shaking his head. 'It's difficult to say, Panos.' He looked up at the size of the hill. 'I can't think it would be a very large tomb,' he said.

'I agree.' said Sarah. 'But it's a tomb of some kind; I'm absolutely sure of it.'

'This excavating which you have done, Mrs Carlos . . . it does seem to reveal a feature that might be the passage leading to the entrance,' Nico conceded after a long thoughtful perusal of the hillside and the scar already made by Sarah. He turned to her, asking if they could get her husband's permission to do some digging. 'We have three weeks,' he said. 'Not a long time, but long enough, if we work from dawn to dusk, for us to determine whether or not it's worth bringing in the archaeologists.'

'I think I'd like to do some work before asking Mr Carlos' permission to . . .' Panos stopped abruptly, faint colour tinting his cheeks. 'I'm sorry, Mrs Carlos. This is your find. It's your decision what shall be done.'

'I'd be glad if you would do some preliminary work

on it,' she agreed at once. 'I'd prefer to establish the fact that it is a grave before I even mention it to my hsuband.'

'So you'll let us come here, every day, and work?' Nico, delighted with her answer, flashed her a broad smile, and added, 'You've said your husband does not know about this yet. Does anyone else know?'

She shook her head. 'No, I haven't mentioned it. As I said, I wanted to make absolutely sure that it was a chamber tomb.' She paused as a thought occurred to her. 'Your mother—and others in the village—they'll wonder where you are all day.'

'Our mother will keep silent if we ask her. As for others—our villa's in a lonely place in the hills. No one will know that we're not at home. In any case, we usually spend much of our time in study, and one seldom sees us in the *taverna*.'

'I'm pretty certain this is a chamber tomb . . .' Panos was speaking to himself, walking about, examining the hill from every aspect.

'I do hope so.' Sarah's excitement was high, encouraged as she was by Panos' words. 'When will you begin digging?'

'As soon as we can get the tools up here,' answered Nico enthusiastically. 'It's fortunate that our house is secluded so we can contrive to smuggle tools and implements up here without attracting any attention.'

They talked for another few minutes, during which the decision was firmly made not to disclose the find to anyone else at this early stage.

'We don't want to look fools,' Sarah added, but she was told by Panos that it would be very unlikely.

'I believe there's a grave of sorts in this hillside. I only wish I could say it was a *tholos* tomb.'

'They wouldn't bury a king on a small island like

this,' put in Sarah. 'No, I feel that it'll turn out to be a chamber tomb.'

'There could still be some fine treasures in it, though.'

'If it hasn't been robbed,' put in Nico with a shake of his head. 'There are very few graves that weren't plundered some time or another.'

'Well, we'll just have to hope it hasn't been fully plundered. There are many tombs like that,' Panos went on, 'otherwise we'd have nothing in the museums.' He looked at his brother. 'Shall we go and get those tools? We could even make a start today, although we haven't a lot of daylight left. However, we'll make a very early start in the morning.'

'I can come up and help you?' Sarah asked uncertainly. She hoped she was not going to be a mere onlooker in the operations.

'It's your find, Mrs Carlos.'

'I know, but I'm not an expert like you.'

'Neither of us is an expert,' Panos denied. 'We're only students.'

'Full-time students, though,' she said, smiling.

'We shall need your help, Mrs Carlos,' Nico assured her, and then, eyeing her curiously, 'You can come up here without your husband knowing?'

'Of course,' she replied, adopting a casual manner. 'My husband works long hours in his study, so I shall be able to come up here for several hours every day, just as I have been doing.' She hoped her explanation was convincing, but she need not have worried, for it seemed that although the question had been asked, her answer went right over their heads, both having bent down again to scrape away at the soil, totally absorbed in their task.

Although Sarah had almost given up hope of rescue as a result of the letter she entrusted to Matthew, and despite the fact that her work on the site had helped to take her mind off her disappointment, she had from the very beginning kept a watchful eye on the clear aquamarine waters between Comaris and the distant shadowy haze that was Rhodes itself, constantly looking for a launch heading towards the island. The site of the chamber tomb was fortunately situated to give a commanding panoramic view over the same stretch of water as the villa, and indeed, from the added height, the silhouette of Rhodes was often clearer than it was from her husband's villa, and she was able to look up from time to time to search the expanse of sea for a boat. She had no idea what the police launch might look like, but had decided that if she did happen to see a boat that was heading this way and that was different from Carl's ferry boat, she would drop whatever she was doing, make a quick apology to Panos and Nico and rush down the hillside in order to be at the villa before the police arrived. They must not interview Carl until she herself had time to talk to them.

By the time a fortnight had passed, it had been established without any doubt at all that a chamber tomb existed beneath the innocent-looking hill. Panos had been able to say for certain that it was a chamber tomb by the style of the passageway leading downwards, into the hillside, towards the entrance to the burial chamber. The passage which had been worked on by the two boys and Sarah was now revealed and was clearly marked, although many more tons of soil would have to be removed before it was cleared sufficiently for the entrance to be found.

'I wish we had more time,' sighed Panos. 'However, we still have a week, so we should be able to move a good proportion of this debris.'

'I think you've done wonders!' Sarah had arrived just a few minutes ago and she stood looking at the two young men as they worked away like navvies with their spades. Then her eyes strayed to the butane stove standing some short distance away, on a flat piece of rock. Beside it were a battered tin kettle, a frying-pan, and another very small, long-handled pan in which they made their syrupy black Turkish coffee. There were several biscuit tins containing sandwiches, and a plastic bag containing fruit.

'Your mother must be a wonder,' she said, taking a pair of garden gloves from the shoulder bag she carried. 'I never really believed we'd be able to keep this thing a secret all this time.'

'Our *mitera* is a wonder,' returned Nico with affection. 'My father, now—if he had been living— could never have kept our secret.' He straightened up as he spoke, squaring his shoulders as if he were finding temporary relief from an aching back. He and his brother were in denims—which by now were looking much the worse for wear—and dark cotton shirts, the sleeves rolled up above the elbows. Sarah rather thought they would have preferred not to wear the shirts but respect for her precluded any thought of discarding them. She had discovered some very charming things about the two cultured, politely spoken young men, one of which was that they hated the dowry system and what it did both to the girl and to the man who married her.

'Why should she have to provide the house, and often land as well?' Panos said angrily. 'And in any case, it's a vicious circle, because when they marry and have daughters, the husband has to work all his life to provide his daughters with houses to give to their husbands when they marry. Pah! It is an outdated custom!'

'Besides that,' supplemented his brother, 'the girl is forced to marry a man she doesn't love. And often the man himself is forced into marriage by his parents. It will die out, this stupid custom. In Greece young people are objecting to the dictatorship of their parents, especially those of us who live in Athens most of the time.'

'So you will both marry for love?' she said, her eyes pensive as she reflected on her own marriage. The marriage she had never wanted—a typical Greek marriage, when one came to think of it, with the bride being forced into it against her will. Sarah supposed that some Greek marriages would turn out all right in the end, with the couple falling in love eventually. But hers . . . ?

This morning Carl had surprised her by asking her to swim with him, and afterwards they had spent the hours till lunch time on the patio, sipping cool drinks from straws and talking, neither noticing just how swiftly the time was passing. Sarah had been strangely happy, not only because of Carl's company but also because he had allowed himself time off to relax, and she hoped it would be the prelude to other such breaks from the dull routine he had been following.

'Yes, we are both determined to marry for love.' Nico's voice drifted into Sarah's train of thought and she looked at him.

'I think there are two very fortunate young ladies somewhere in Greece,' she returned, a laugh on her lips but a serious expression in her eyes.

'We cannot marry for a long while yet. We have

much work to do before we shall be in a position to marry.'

Sarah looked at the part they had uncovered, and thought again how incredible it was that they had removed so much earth in such a short time. She had helped, carrying away the earth in the small wheel-barrow they had brought up, and as she worked like a labourer Sarah could not help but feel a tingle of apprehension at the idea of Carl finding out what she was doing. Yet there was nothing demeaning in such work; she had done it many times before, when working on digs in England.

'If we are lucky enough to find a treasure,' she said, glancing at the wall again, 'you'll be rich.'

'This land belongs to Mr Carlos. But in any case, any treasures will go into the museums.'

'You'll get something, surely?'

'A reward, but that will be yours, for it was your discovery.'

'I don't want any reward,' she began, then stopped abruptly as an idea occurred to her. If she could get her hands on something valuable, she might be able to use it as a bribe to enable her to get away from Carl. A bribe to whom, though? Yannis' name seemed to emerge from her subconscious, and she knew instinctively that if the bribe were large enough he would accept it.

An eye for an eye. Carl had bribed Eric to leave her here, and she could bribe Yannis to help her get away . . .

But did she still want to get away? Almost angrily she put the question from her, vehemently telling herself that no matter how she felt about the changes taking place in Carl and herself, she still wanted to get off this island.

The following morning she went along to Maroula's villa, but Maroula had still not returned. And with several weeks having passed, Sarah was becoming filled with apprehension in case Matthew should decide to write to her, explaining why his aunt had not returned to Comaris. Carl would get hold of the letter, simply because the bag with the letters for the villa—be they his or his servants'—was brought up from the ferry when it came in from Rhodes.

The matter troubled Sarah for several days, but, deciding she could do nothing about it if Matthew did write and his letter came into Carl's possession, she sensibly put it out of her mind. It would be time enough to worry about it if, and when, it happened.

Chapter Nine

The last day had arrived, and although ton upon ton of earth had been removed by the two brothers, there was not a lot to see for all their hard work. Sarah, too, had toiled like a Trojan, taking away one barrowload of soil after another and dumping it a small distance away. Working together as they were, all equally engrossed in the excavation, it was natural that a camaraderie should have grown up between them, and it was with as much regret as they that Sarah began to collect up the implements and other tackle and pile it into the wheelbarrow. Either Panos or Nico would come up after dark and take it down to his mother's house.

'It's sad, isn't it, that we haven't more time?' said Panos. 'You'll have to tell your husband now,' he went on, turning to Sarah. 'The experts ought to be brought in.'

Sarah nodded in agreement, her eyes moving to that small section of the *dromos* on which they had been working. At the end of it would be the entrance, and beyond it the bee-hive-shaped tomb where lay the remains of whoever was buried there, and those treasures they had particularly valued in life—if the grave robbers had not been at work.

'When shall you be here again?' Sarah asked when at last they were all ready to leave the side.

'Our next vacation's at Christmas.'

'If the archaeologists are here then, you'll help, of course?' She did not want the site to be fully excavated without their further help. They had done so much work that it seemed unfair for someone else to come along and take over completely. It would all depend on Carlos, of course, but Sarah felt sure that when she showed him just how much had been done he would agree that the two boys must be brought into the project whenever they were on the island.

'We hope to help, yes,' replied Nico eagerly. 'I'd love to be around when the entrance is breached, but more than likely we shan't be on vacation at that particular time.'

Sarah made no comment. She might not be around herself at that time, for it could be a year or more before the passage was completely uncovered. It depended not only on how long it happened to be but also on the number of people working on it.

'Well, this is good-bye.' Panos stood looking at Sarah, sadness invading his dark, long-lashed eyes.

'But we shall meet again, of course,' he added, and it was plain that he was trying to sound cheerful.

Again Sarah said nothing, but she did nod her head in a gesture of reassurance on noticing Panos' inquiring expression.

The last good-byes were said and Sarah stood alone when the two youths left her, watching them move slowly away, until, just before they were to become lost to view in the trees, they turned and waved at her.

She turned then, feeling ineffably flat and depressed as she wondered what she would do with her time. Perhaps Maroula had returned, in which case she would at least have someone to talk to now and then. But when, the following morning, she went along the shore to the villa, it was only to find it looking as deserted as before, and with the flowers in the garden being choked by weeds. She would bring a small fork and trowel and get some of the weeds up, she decided, exceedingly puzzled about Maroula's continued absence. It was very strange that she had not returned before now. Matthew had been so sure that she would be home two days after he left.

During the three weeks when the excavation was taking place, Sarah had had no difficulty in spending most of her mornings and afternoons up at the site, Carl as usual going to his study immediately after breakfast and not leaving it until one o'clock, when Sarah would join him for lunch. By about a quarter to two he was back in his study, where he would remain until six o'clock at the earliest. He was usually very quiet, but occasionally he did open up a conversation, and he would usually begin by asking Sarah what she had been doing with herself, which was the last question she wanted him to ask, as it always necessitated a lie.

'Reading and walking,' she would answer, 'and sometimes I go down to the harbour and watch the ferry coming or going.'

'And wishing you were on it when it's going?' He watched her closely when this question was asked, one day when he had sat rather longer than usual over lunch.

'Naturally I wish I was leaving Comaris,' she answered; yet even as she spoke, a doubt lingered in her mind.

She could not visualise the actual moment of leaving, of voicing the triumphant good-bye which at first had been an obsession. She had even rehearsed what she would say to Carl: 'There's your child—the payment for my freedom. I hope you'll have some feasible explanation when the time comes for him to ask about his mother!'

Would those words ever be uttered now? First, there was no sign of a child, and secondly, Sarah was very doubtful of ever uttering words like them even if she did oblige her husband and produce a son.

'Naturally you wish to leave . . .' Carl repeated her words slowly to himself, a strange play of emotions in his black, pitchblende eyes. 'So nothing has changed?' He looked at her then, his expression inscrutable.

'Changed, Carl?' she echoed, feigning puzzlement.

'You've seemed more settled lately.' Carl reached over to help himself to more cheese. 'You haven't been as restless as you were.' His eyes met hers across the table, then fell, to linger on the seductive, peach-toned valley between her breasts. She wondered what he would have to say if she enlightened him as to the reason why she had been more settled. He obviously believed the change in her had something to do with him, and she was recalling something he had said to her a few nights ago, when, desire fulfilled and passion spent, he had held her in his arms, relaxing the whole naked length of his body against hers.

'You need me physically, Sarah, just as I need you. And whether a child comes to us or not, I believe you'll stay with me.'

Sarah, recovering from the violent storm of her own unbridled passion, had no wish to refute his assertion.

'I suppose I am more resigned than I was,' she admitted frankly, meeting his eyes across the table. 'Nevertheless,' she went on to say, 'freedom is still the most important thing in my mind.'

Carl had lapsed into a silence that lasted until they both left the table, he to go to his study and Sarah to change into denims and a shirt and make her eager way into the forested hills towards the one special hill under which might be buried treasures untold.

Sarah could not have said why she hesitated about telling Carl of the find she had made and the work done on it since. He had become morose again, scarcely speaking, and it was natural that she was assailed by apprehension every time she thought of telling him of the tomb's existence. It caused her to be confused and always in a state of indecision, feeling on the one hand that he would be exceedingly interested in the find, and that this would make inroads into the moroseness that seemed always to be with him these days, but on the other hand there was the possibility of his being furious at not being brought into the picture right at the beginning. Looking back now, Sarah was conscious of a feeling of underhandedness about keeping her husband in the dark, and yet it was by no means intentional. As she had told Panos and Nico, she wanted to make sure that there really was something of importance beneath the hill before approaching Carl and asking him to call in the experts and have the whole site excavated.

It was a week after the departure of Panos and Nico that Sarah, having decided to go up and take a look at the site, just for something to do, arrived back home to be told by Androula that Carl wanted to see her.

'Mr Carlos said I must watch for you and tell you he wants you urgently in his study.'

'Thank you, Androula.' Sarah's heart had turned a somersault on hearing the word 'urgently,' and as she hurried towards the door through which she had never passed up till now, she was conscious of a similar premonition of danger as that which had assailed her when she knew she was to meet Carl again after an interval of seven years.

She knocked somewhat timidly but received no answer. She knocked again, a little louder. Still no answer, and after a small hesitation she turned the knob and swung the door inwards. Carl was not there . . . and yet he had said he wanted to see her urgently. She would wait, she decided, moving towards the massive leather-topped antique desk. There was an assortment of papers on it which seemed to have been pushed to one side, isolating one single sheet which held prominence in front of the place where Carl was obviously sitting. Sarah was just in the act of taking possession of the chair on the opposite side of the desk when she caught sight of the name at the bottom of the letter.

'Matthew!' Her heart lurched as she realised that what she had feared had come about. Anger plucked

her senses at the idea that Carl should have opened
her letter, even though it was to be expected that he
would do so.

She reached for the letter and read,

Dear Sarah,
I thought I had better write to explain why
Aunt Maroula hasn't yet returned to Comaris.
She took ill in London the day before she was to
fly to Athens. There was a cable waiting for me
at the hotel where we were to meet. She had had
a heart attack and was in hospital. I flew home
immediately and went to see her. She would
recover, I was told, but she must not travel for
several weeks. So she is with me in my flat. I'm
so sorry not to have written before, but what
with all the upset, and my not being used to any
sort of upheaval, I suppose I am not coping very
well. I hope to see you in the not-too-distant
future, as my boss has kindly said I can have
time off to accompany my aunt back to Comaris
when she is well enough to travel.

                              Kind regards
                              Matthew.

No mention of the letter she had given him to post.
It had obviously gone right out of his mind in his
anxiety over his aunt, but where was it now? Sarah
was forced to accept that he had probably lost it.

She held the paper in trembling fingers, an ache in
her throat born of fear. How was she going to explain?
And what was to be the outcome of this? Would Carl
curtail her freedom?

She jumped visibly as the door opened behind her.

'So you've arrived.' The door snapped shut with a click that made Sarah jump again. She turned, and at his expression she went white, a hand stealing to her throat. She rose unsteadily to her feet, for what reason she could not have said.

'So you've read the letter?' Carl's eyes flickered to the desk. 'Who is this man and how does he come to be writing to you? I beileve I asked you, some time ago, if you'd met Maroula?'

'Yes, y-you d-did.' She could scarcely articulate words, the dryness in her throat affecting the tender membranes like a rasp. 'I haven't met her,' she quivered, backing away strategically as he advanced into the room. 'Matthew's her . . . her nephew. You . . . haven't met him . . . obviously?'

'When did *you* meet him?' he gritted, ignoring her question. 'When and where? Answer me!'

She shivered, and a wave of tears threatened. But by a tremendous effort she contrived to appear calm under the burning vapour of fury that looked out of his eyes.

'He was staying at Maroula's villa. She and he had exchanged accommodation because she wanted to have a holiday in London. Matthew and I met when I was taking a walk along the beach. He's English, and s-so . . .' She stopped, still battling with her fear. 'It was natural that we . . . we would speak, and become friendly—'

'How friendly?' interrupted Carl, a dangerous softness in his foreign voice. 'How long was he there?'

'A month.'

'A month?' White drifts of fury stole along the sides of his mouth. 'You knew him for a whole month?'

'He'd already been there for five days when we met.'

'I asked you how friendly you were.' He had come

closer, to tower above her, a darkly menacing figure, his pagan eyes like pools of molten lava, and as destructive.

'We had coffee together on several occasions, that's all.'

'When did he leave?' Again Carl spoke softly, his lips drawn tight.

'About a month ago.'

'And this is the first time you've heard from him?'

'It must be, mustn't it? All letters come here, to you.'

'What exactly does this letter explain?' he wanted to know.

'It's perfectly clear. He'd told me I must meet his aunt when she returned to Comaris. He would be seeing her in Athens and would tell her about me.'

'He knew you were married to me?'

'Yes, I told him.'

'When was this?'

'The first morning after . . . after our marriage.'

'The morning? What time?'

'Very early. I was out at half-past seven.'

'Did he know how long we'd been married?'

'Yes, I told him we were married at three o'clock the previous afternoon.'

The black eyes narrowed thoughtfully. 'He must have considered it very strange—a bride of one night walking alone along the seashore at that time of the morning.'

'He probably did.' She was very much calmer now, and her colour had returned.

'He didn't question you?'

'Matthew is a very reserved young man. Whatever his thoughts about my being out so early in the mornings, he kept them to himself.'

'I see . . .' His eyes bored into hers, as if they would

see right into her very soul. She met his gaze unflinchingly, and at last his thick lashes came down.

'You obviously did not ask him for help, then?'

She shook her head.

'How could I? I have my pride. No, I did not ask him for help.'

'I believe you,' he said, and it did seem that his manner was slightly less hostile. 'Nevertheless, it seems incredible to me that you did not seek his help.' He lifted a questioning brow. 'Why didn't you?'

'I've just said—I have my pride. It would have been impossible to have asked a total stranger for help.' Was she convincing? With a palpitating heart she watched his face, alert for any change of expression that would warn her of danger. But he no longer seemed angry, a circumstance for which she sent up a fervent little prayer of thankfulness.

'He wasn't a stranger by the time he left, though.'

'No . . . but neither was he a friend—at least, not the sort of friend one could confide in. He never knew that I . . . we . . . weren't happy.'

'You mean you didn't tell him we weren't happy?'

'No,' she answered, thankful to be telling the truth, for to lie to anyone as shrewd as her husband was not only a strain but it was also taking a great risk. 'It would have seemed too absurd, anyway—our having been so recently married.'

'He must have suspected that something was wrong?'

'I . . . er . . . don't know . . .'

'He'd be damned obtuse if he didn't.' Carl walked over to the desk and flipped the letter to the opposite side. 'Here, take it—and watch your step in the future. This will have proved to you that correspondence with anyone outside this island without my knowing is an impossibility. Don't try anything or by God you'll regret it.'

Sarah could never afterwards remember just when it was that she began to regard her husband as a lover and a friend rather than the avenger he had set himself out to be. She had previously asked herself if the new emotions she was experiencing could be the beginnings of love, and had come to the brink of admitting they were, but had managed to hold back, vitally conscious of the fact that a categorical admission of love would be one for which she would despise herself.

But now . . . She was on the patio watching the tall gaunt figure of her husband as he wandered aimlessly among the flower beds and borders, appearing neither to see nor to hear anything that was going on around him—the glory of an exotic garden superbly kept, the perfumes carried from one magnificent flower bed to another, all mingling to produce nature's own unique blend, a heady perfume excelling any that man could possibly devise. Nor did he hear the birds and the crickets, the mournful bray of the lonely donkey on the hill, the sweet tinkle of goat bells on the necks of animals wandering over lush green pastures, cropping grass. He was a man apart, both from nature and from his own kind. Sarah felt a tremor of pity ripple through her, knew a desperate longing to run out to him and hold him close, to cradle his dark head upon her breast, to whisper to him, begging him not to brood upon the past but to reach out and grasp what the future had to offer him.

Just what did the future have to offer him? He was hoping for a son. And if he should get that son, he was then intending to bring him up alone. He would have a nanny, then perhaps a tutor, or maybe Carl would send his child to a boarding school in Athens . . .

Had Carl really looked into this future he was planning for himself? Had he seen the futility, the aimless path which led through fruitless years to a void of loneliness worse than any he had known before, simply because his son would leave him, as all sons do, and Carl would be condemned to solitude again?

The more she thought about Carl's plight, the more terrible it appeared, until a wave of pity stronger than any she had known before impelled her to get up and go to him. He was her husband; it was her privilege to comfort him . . .

He heard her soft approach and turned his head. She smiled across the small distance separating them, quickening her pace so as to reach him before he hurried on, silently telling her to go away and leave him alone.

'Can I walk with you, Carl?' she asked, a little breathless as she reached his side. She lifted beautiful blue eyes to his dark and sombre face, and added, 'It's such a lovely afternoon, isn't it?'

He seemed puzzled, but not exceptionally so, simply owing to the change that had recently come over them both. Beginning as an almost imperceptible change—a sort of dawning tolerance each for the other—it had grown in strength despite the setbacks caused by Carl, who seemed as if he despised himself for what could be a weakness. Sarah had the impression that the friendliness and gentleness he showed towards her on occasion were almost immediately regretted. But she had persevered, resolved as she was not to hurt him, and so there began to be some bright spots in their relationship—albeit these were still quite rare. Hitherto, Sarah, once she had become resigned to the fact that there was no escape until she did have his child, had wanted to get the whole thing over and done with so that she would gain her release from what, at that time, was sheer hell.

But it was no longer hell. For one thing, now she never cringed at his approach, wishing it was all over and she would be left alone. No, she actually waited in eagerness for the moment when he would come from his own room into hers. Aware of the ascendancy he had gained over her, he would sometimes gloat and sneer, and his hands would be cruel, yet at other times he was the gentle lover, and there had been occasions recently when Sarah would not have been surprised to hear an endearment escape his lips when, having made love to her, he would hold her for a little while in his arms, his dark face nestling close to her breast.

'A lovely afternoon . . .' His voice brought her from her reverie, and she glanced up at him, her eyes bright and clear, her lovely hair teased by the wind. 'Yes, I suppose it is. But I was thinking of going in,' he added, just as if he had to in order to give the impression that he did not want her company. But Sarah, with the keen perception that had come to her lately, believed she understood his mood. Well, if she must meet him half way, then she would—even more than half way if it were necessary.

'Please stay with me for a little while, Carl.' Moving closer, she got a whiff of the musky male smell of him that never failed to stir her senses. 'You have no need to go back to work yet, surely?' Her fluttering smile found a thin response in the curve of his full-lipped, sensuous mouth. It was one of his rare smiles which, of late, had brought light into her life, if only fleetingly.

His downward, slanting glance was guarded, though, and she accepted that his emotions were not for revealing.

'Very well—but only for a few minutes.'

They walked about the grounds in total silence, and perhaps it was inevitable that Sarah should begin to ask herself if this was what she really wanted—to be the companion of a man who would not even speak to her. Her upward glance caught a picture of cold hard features arrogantly impassive, and a stony gaze focused on nothing in particular. Strange, unfathomable man! It seemed impossible that he was once young and happy . . . and inexpressibly handsome.

She could have had him then, when she did not want him. And now . . . ? Did she want him? If he were as attractive and loving as before, then yes! There, the admission was made at last, the admission that she had made a mistake in refusing him. But she was only eighteen at the time, an absurd age in which to make a decision that would have affected her whole life. Why had he not come two or three years later, when she was more mature?

Fate—capricious, inexorable fate—had willed it otherwise.

'What are you thinking about?' Carl's voice cut softly into her thoughts and she answered without hesitation, 'Us, and what fate has done to us.'

'Fate?' with a tilt of his straight black brows. 'I seem to remember your saying that each of us is the captain of his or her own soul. Decisions are made by individuals. What has fate to do with us?'

'It wasn't my decision that I marry you, Carl.'

'It was mine. Fate had nothing to do with it.'

She fell silent. They had slowed their steps as they approached the place where the villa grounds met the beach, and she expected Carl to say they would turn back. But he merely stopped, his eyes turned towards the sea as if watching its deep, gem-blue colour being changed all the time by the quivering pulsation of light and shade produced when the scudding wisps of fair-weather cumulus intruded into the sapphire brilliance of the sky.

'Shall we walk along the beach?' ventured Sarah when at last the wordless silence stretched beyond endurance.

Carl's black eyes looked down, boring uncomfortably into hers. 'What are you trying to do?' he asked disconcertingly.

'There's nothing expecially significant in my asking you to take a stroll with me, Carl.'

'Is it pity you feel for me?' His voice was suddenly harsh, and the swift impatient movement of his body indicated an impulse to turn around and make his way back to the house.

'We both need pity, Carl,' she answered gently. 'I've already told you that.'

'When you mentioned fate.' It was not a question, so she offered no response. 'Was it fate that made you marry someone else a few weeks after you'd refused me?' So quiet, the foreign voice, but latent fury vibrated through it. 'No, Sarah, it was your decision. He was a millionaire, a good catch from any gold-digger's point of view—'

'I'm not a gold-digger!' she broke in fiercely. 'You shan't call me that!'

'What else are you, then?' The cold sneer in his

voice brought ice to her heart. 'But you were well paid out, weren't you? Nothing!' He paused to laugh in her face. 'All your scheming, and he left you nothing!'

She opened her mouth to blurt out the truth, then changed her mind. She had asked herself a few minutes ago if this was really what she wanted—to be with a man who had no desire whatsoever for her company. No, this was *not* what she wanted. Physically Carl might draw her, but there was more to marriage than going to bed. There should be companionship and closeness. There should be constant loving and caring and planning. There were adventures to share through rain and shine, problems to solve and trials to overcome. And always the clasp of a hand for comfort.

No, life with Carl was not what she wanted. And as they walked in silence back to the house, Sarah's mind turned once more to thoughts of escape.

Matthew was coming back soon, to bring his aunt. Sarah decided to give him another letter to post for her.

Chapter Ten

Dinner that evening was a silent meal, with Carl so morose that Sarah felt convinced he would not come to her room later, when they went to bed. It would not be the first time; he had been particularly morose like this before, and on each occasion had bidden her a curt good night and left her—to go either to his study or to his own bedroom, Sarah hadn't known which. It was, therefore, a surprise when she heard the door between the rooms open and saw Carl standing there, his hands thrust into the pockets of a black silk dressing-gown.

'Oh . . . I thought you . . . er . . . were tired.' Having resigned herself to his not coming, she was now annoyed that he had come, which was all very illogical, she had to admit, because it wasn't as if there was any doubt about her enjoyment of his love-making.

'Is that your way of telling me that *you* are tired?' His expression of taunting amusement brought angry colour to her cheeks.

'If I were tired, I should say so,' she snapped. 'I don't have to resort to subterfuge!'

'It wouldn't do you much good if you did.' As he came farther into the room the girdle of his dressing-gown slipped and the gown came open, revealing the rippling muscles of his torso. He stood for a long moment in possessive contemplation of her body. She was silhouetted in the heavy, gilt-framed mirror of the dressing-table, the subtle rose glow from the lamps on either side of the frame tinting her face and the gold of her hair, and accentuating the slim seductive lines of the feminine contours revealed through the clinging chiffon swathe of her long nightdress. Her eyes slid to the dainty cotton housecoat she had bought recently from Theodora's boutique, but she made no move to pick it up, knowing full well that her husband would be there before her to snatch it from her reach. He was revelling in what he considered to be his; Sarah knew she would not be allowed to hide her beauty from his gaze. It was transferred to her face; she saw the arrogant twist of his mouth that spelled both superiority and dominance before the black pagan eyes moved slowly downwards from the delicately moulded breasts to the slender waist, and lastly, to the outlined contours of her hips and thighs. She looked at him, conscious of tingling nerves, of the atmosphere between them being electrically charged, ready to ignite. His eyes roved again, coming upwards now from the dainty, pink-tinted toe-nails to the tantalising burrow between her breasts. How typically Greek! No wonder they had been described as the most amorous race in the world! She felt her colour rise and averted her head, embarrassed without knowing why. She had been subjected to this kind of examination so many times before. She felt a hand on her wrist drawing her away from the dressing-table, and another hand beneath her chin, an imperious, masterful touch, and she lifted her head again in meek obedience to the silent command. Anger surged at the arrogance of his every gesture, at the half-sneering expression of the conqueror that looked out from the depths of eyes as hard as stone, and for an unguarded instant she made a move as if to twist away. But she held back just in time, remembering all too well the punishment he meted out in response to what he had once described as her 'intolerable English defiance.'

He bent to kiss her, the smoothness of his full wide lips sliding moistly over hers—the first stimulus designed to awaken her senses. His hands slid to her waist; she knew the pleasure-pain of lean, sensitive fingers trying to span it before they moved downwards to pause momentarily at the sharp contraction of her stomach muscles beneath their palms. As they began to slide down farther, Sarah did then twist away in a swift instinctive movement, but her wrist was caught in a grip that brought a protesting cry to her lips and a tear to her eye.

'You're hurting me—!' The rest was jerked to silence as his arms came round her, searing her flesh in a vise-like embrace that threatened to crush her body to pulp. She felt the probe of his tongue at the same time that his ravenous mouth brought fire into her lips. The musky odour of him assailing her nostrils, heady and male, was seduction itself, igniting the flame of her own desire, affecting every nerve and tissue in her body. A spasm of expectancy awoke her senses as his roving hand, dispensing with a shoulder strap, slid possessively into the front of her nightdress. He bent his head, and seconds later she felt the scorching sear of his mouth as it widened to take its avid fill of the heady sweetness of her breast.

She arched her body, experiencing exquisite pain from the granite hardness of his loins as they pressed their urgent need against the fine silk skin that was the only barrier between his flesh and hers.

'You're more vitally alive every time I come to you!' The passion vibrating through him lent a hoarseness to his voice, and it sounded more foreign than ever. His dark face, too, was alien, its pagan lines and contours seeming almost unfamiliar when viewed through the glaze of passion in her eyes. 'Alive, Sarah, and responsive! I little knew when I planned for you to give me a son that I'd have this bonus thrown in!' With hunger as the spur, he swept her into his arms, carried her to the bed and within moments their bodies were convulsed, melting into one, as fulfillment carried them to the heights of ecstasy.

Half an hour later she was alone, her hands limp on the bed cover, her body relaxed but her mind disturbed. Physical satisfaction without mutual love.

. . . What was it worth? Little had she known when
first she learned what was in store for her, that she
would fall madly in love with the man whose captive
she had become. Love had never before entered into
her scheme of things, and if she did happen to think
about falling in love, it was always something that
happened to someone else—never her. Now she was
wildly in love with a man who was himself incapable
of love. Sarah was more sure than ever that, despite
her deep love for her husband, she must get away
from him just as soon as the opportunity arose. She
wished she had some idea of when Matthew would be
here. It surely could not be long now, she thought,
and decided that from now on she would go down and
meet every ferry that sailed into the harbour of
Comaris.

The following morning Sarah went along to
Maroula's villa, taking a small fork and trowel. A
couple of hours spent on the front borders worked
wonders, and she stood back to regard the flower beds
with satisfaction. She would come again tomorrow
and do some work on the side, then progress to the
back by degrees. This hard physical work seemed to
suit her, she thought, ruefully reflecting on the work
she had done up at the site of the tomb. She must go
up and see that everything was all right, she decided,
and she must also be making up her mind about
telling Carl. For although it was most improbable that
the site would be discovered by any inhabitant of the
island, its location being not only isolated but also
hidden by trees, it certainly was not impossible for
anyone to come upon it. She herself had wandered up
there, and so had the two boys. Besides, Panos and

Nico would be expecting things to be happening, and looking forward to the Christmas vacation when they would again be able to go up there and dig.

She went up the following afternoon, climbing into the forested region, making for the plateau behind which was the hill. Going was much more difficult than before owing to the effects of the torrential rain that had fallen during the night. But she made it at last, only to stand and stare at the site. Masses of loose soil had been washed away from the exposed wall of the *dromos*, and as she stood staring, her eyes became focused on something shining in the sunlight. She went forward to investigate, probing with her fingers in the soil which was now turned to mud.

'It's . . . gold . . .' Her pulses quickened; in a sort of desperate haste she went to the flat stone under which her two implements had been hidden by Nico when Sarah had told him she wasn't taking them home yet. She picked up the spade, but the instant she began to use it she stopped, catching her breath. This was no task for a clumsy spade. . . . She would use her hands.

A few minutes later she was staring down in wonderment at the incredibly beautiful gold bracelet which had obviously been fashioned for male wear. She had wiped it on her handkerchief, but mud still adhered to the rosette which decorated the front; and in the crevices of the fine gold workings, the dirt was ingrained and hard.

The presence of the bracelet near the wall of the passage was clear evidence that the grave had been robbed in antiquity, the thieves having dropped it in their hurry to get away from the scene of their crime without delay. How much had they taken, she wondered, thinking of the disappointment of the two brothers if everything except this bracelet had been stolen.

She stood for a long while, the bracelet in her hand, dwelling on the far-distant past when some artist had cleverly fashioned this beautiful piece of jewelry. For whom? . . . A warrior perhaps, who had worn it on the upper arm? And now the warrior's bones lay within that chamber . . .

At last she wrapped the precious object in her handkerchief and put it in her pocket. What would she do with it? Now, surely, was the time to enlighten Carl, showing him the find and asking what he intended to do about the excavation of the tomb.

But hammering at her brain was an altogether different idea. . . . This find would buy her freedom. . . . But there were two problems. the first being her conscience, the bracelet not being her property, and the second was: how to approach her husband's servant, Yannis.

Several days went by with Sarah in a state of indecision, resolving one moment that she would wait until Matthew came back, when he could take another letter for her and post it to Avril. But the next moment she was remembering that the first letter had gone astray and that a second one might not reach its destination either. It was very unlikely, but possible. Also, it could be months before Matthew returned—another unlikely occurrence, but again, possible. His aunt could remain unfit to travel for some considerable time to come.

Why take a chance when she might have the opportunity of an earlier escape? There was still no

sign of a child, and if she could leave now. . . . It was
of course possible that Yannis would flatly refuse his
help, but Sarah rather thought that a servant who
would discuss his employer in the way he had done
would not be troubled by a sense of loyalty when
offered a prize as valuable as the one Sarah had in her
possession. She had not had very much to do with
Yannis, but she had learned, one day when she had
chatted to him in the garden, that he had two sisters
needing dowries, a circumstance that was certainly in
Sarah's favour, since Yannis could not marry until his
sisters had found husbands. This was the custom in
many Greek villages, where brothers had to work to
provide their sisters with dowries, and it certainly
applied in the remote village in the Peloponnese
where Yannis came from and where his family still
lived.

But there was the problem of approaching him
with her request, and the days lengthened to a
week and still she had not found a way out of her
difficulty.

Not once during this time did it dawn on her that
her preoccupation would be noticed by Carl, even
though she was often mystified by the strange,
all-examining glances he cast in her direction. One
evening, however, he said right out of the blue,
'There's something on your mind, Sarah.' They were
in the lounge, and he spoke from the other side of the
room, where he was mixing a cocktail. 'I'd like to
know what it is.'

A creamy pallor fused her cheeks, but she managed
to feign surprise as she said, 'I don't know what you
mean, Carl. If it's that I haven't talked much—well,
you and I never do talk much, do we?'

He stood with an empty glass in his hand, his eyes narrowed as they searched her face. 'Don't prevaricate,' he warned. 'I'm not a fool. You're different lately—restless again. There was a time when you were settled—'

'I've never been settled,' she broke in to deny. 'You must be stupid to assume I could be settled with things as they are.'

'As they are?' he repeated sharply.

Sarah hesitated. It was a tense moment, as they stared at one another across the lovely room, its hidden lights and candleglow lending a softness to the atmosphere . . . and a sort of gentle magic. Sarah felt that if only she knew how to handle this situation, all would be well between her husband and herself.

But she did not know how to handle it, and in any case, the moment was lost when Carl, indifferent to the answer for which he had seemed to be waiting with such interest, added shortly, 'What is it you want? You've a good life—every luxury, nothing to do. You wanted to marry money—well, you've done so. Many women would be more than content to be in your position.' His back was to the high window, and through it could be seen the clear outline of a full moon rising in the dark sky. Crystalline and vibrant, it showered the garden with an argent brilliancy cut here and there by the shapes of trees looming up, throwing their shadows across the lawn and towards the window. Caught in these shadows, Carl's face took on a repellant aspect, its features distorted into almost evil lines.

'Many women would be more than content to be in my position. . . .' Sarah repeated the words mechanically, her eyes still fixed on her husband's formidable countenance. 'Carl,' she added softly, 'I'm a prisoner. How could I be content?'

'You still regard yourself as a prisoner?' He was frowning in an abstract way, and as she continued to watch him, Sarah saw to her surprise that he had little grey lines at the corners of his mouth, as if he were in the grip of some painfully strong emotion. He half-filled the glass and brought it over to her. 'I've asked you a question,' he said.

'Of course I regard myself as a prisoner.' She spread her hands impatiently. 'I *am* a prisoner.'

'You're free to go anywhere on this island.'

'But not free to leave you.' She looked up, accepting the glass he was offering her.

'When you give me a child you'll be free,' he said inexorable, 'and not before.'

She said after a small hesitation, 'Has it occurred to you that I might be unable to have a child?'

He seemed to flinch, she thought, and those black eyes appeared for a second to be devoid of all hope. Yet his words belied this impression as he said, 'It has, but I've dismissed it. I can't believe that a woman like you could be barren.'

It was Sarah's turn to flinch, for she had always detested the word. It had a stigma about it, a taint of some kind.

'It happens all the time, Carl,' she said after a pause. 'Many women are unable to have children.'

He fell silent, sipping the drink he had poured himself; his face was impassive, but a movement at the side of his jaw gave Sarah the impression that he was more deeply affected by her words than he would ever admit. Perhaps he would dwell on them and brood over them and in the end decide to let her go. . . . She shook her head. His desire for her would make him keep her here. Hadn't he once said that even if they did not have a child she would never leave him? What he had really meant was that he would never let her go.

Chapter Eleven

In spite of her firm resolution to escape by the swiftest possible means, Sarah still suffered some heart-searchings regarding the action she contemplated. For one thing, she had difficulty in shaking off her guilt complex, being faced with the knowledge that if she had married Carl all those years ago, he would not now be carrying this burden of mental torture.

For another thing, the very idea of leaving Carl alone and unhappy in his misery was excruciatingly painful, even to the extent that she would find herself shaking her head and whispering fiercely, 'I can't do it! He has no one in the whole world but me, and I can't desert him!' But immediately upon this there would rise, inescapably, a picture of her own life, and she would have to ask herself if her pity was strong enough for her to sacrifice this life. She was wise enough to know that even a love as strong as hers needed reciprocation and nurturing if it was to survive; without that it must inevitably wither and die.

As a preliminary to her request to Yannis, she chatted with him rather more than usual when he was in the garden, helping with the weeds or performing other chores such as pruning roses or removing dead flowers from the beds and borders. And during these chats she discovered a shady character beneath the ready smiles and the ability he had of meeting her gaze with apparent frankness and sincerity. She discovered that he was envious of his employer, and she became convinced that he would be only too eager to leave him if he could.

Yes, she mused one day as she watched him at the task of cleaning windows, he would seize an opportunity of getting away from his employer, and with this knowledge firmly in her mind, she wondered why she still hesitated. The time to act was now . . . and yet. . . .

A deep sigh escaped her as her pensive gaze became fixed on the window which Yannis dared not clean while the room was occupied. Carl's study, where he spent long lonely hours, day in, day out. And by his own admission he had followed this pattern of life for the past three years. Three years! And yet it could go on for ten times that long. Sarah shivered, as if the sun had suddenly been obscured by a black, ice-filled cloud.

Over lunch he spoke again about her restlessness, even going as far as asking her outright if she were planning something.

Her natural reaction was to dissemble, and she echoed, feigning surprise, 'Planning? I don't know what you mean, Carl.'

'Always the air of innocence,' he sneered. 'I've effectively closed every avenue of escape, so if you've any ideas of getting off this island, then you can put them right out of your mind.' His face was a dark mask, inscrutable and harsh.

'In that case,' she countered, 'what are you worrying about?'

His eyes narrowed to little more than slits. 'I'm warning you,' he said, as if she had not spoken, 'if you so much as try to get away from me, I'll keep you prisoner in the house.'

He would, too; she had no doubts about that. She thought of her idea to enlist help from his servant and shivered inwardly at the picture of its going wrong and their both being caught in the act by Carl.

'I asked what you were worrying about,' repeated Sarah. 'You can't be totally confident of your ability to keep me here, can you?'

He had been eating, but the knife and fork were now idle in his hands. He spoke harshly, ignoring what she had said. 'That Englishman who wrote to you has written again—'

'Again?' She drew a frightened breath, her first reaction being that Matthew had mentioned the letter and offered her an apology. But instantly she forgot the idea; Carl would not be so calm as this if he had learned of the letter she had asked Matthew to post. 'What has he to say?' Aware that a show of indignation at Carl's opening a letter addressed to her would prove totally ineffective, Sarah let the matter pass as she continued, 'Is Maroula well enough to come home?'

'No. Her nephew writes to say she is staying with him indefinitely.'

Sarah froze. There was a significant undertone to his voice that caused her to regard him suspiciously. 'You had something to do with it?' Carl remained silent, and she added, trying to penetrate the dark inscrutable depths of his eyes, 'What about her villa? Is she selling it?'

'She wants me to arrange for someone to go in and look after it.' A hint of mocking triumph had crept into his voice, and it was not difficult for Sarah to guess what he had meant just now when he said he had closed every avenue of escape.

'You've obviously been in touch with her.' Sarah toyed with her food, starkly conscious of the fact that her husband had not treated her association with Matthew with the indifference she had been foolish enough to assume.

'I was more perturbed than I appeared when I learned that an Englishman had been in Maroula's villa and that you had met him. It seemed unnatural that you would not try to enlist his help in effecting the escape which, at that time, was nothing less than an obsession. I believed you when you said you had not attempted to enlist his help, but that did not alter the fact that I considered it very strange you did not grasp an opportunity that seemed so obvious.' He was watching her intently as he continued, 'I could not believe—seeing that you are not expecting a child— that you would allow a second opportunity to pass you by. When this Matthew returned with his aunt, you and he would be more friendly than before, because you'd had a start, so to speak. It seemed to me that you would now confide in him and seek his assistance in getting away from me.' His mouth tightened as he saw the guilty colour stealing into the pallor of her face. 'However, in order to prevent this from happening, I have written to Maroula advising her to remain with her nephew for the time being—'

'It was an order,' she broke in angrily, 'not really advice?'

'I said it was my wish that she stay away for a while. I pointed out that she could not now live alone in that isolated place; she would be too much of a responsibility to me, because I should be continually anxious about her and as a result would have to send someone along to her villa at least once every day. She's a very sensible lady,' Carl went on reflectively, 'and will see my point of view. She also has a great respect for my authority as owner of Comaris.'

'You put it very well,' she flashed, anger bringing a quiver to her voice. 'But it's no less than dictatorship!'

'Call it what you like.' He shrugged, and then, when she did not speak: 'You will have great difficulty in taking me unawares, Sarah,' he warned, his eyes never leaving her face as, mechanically, he helped himself to more vegetables from the dish that was standing over a silver spirit stove. 'How you must be regretting the lost opportunity,' he said, just as if he had to gloat, reminding her that she had committed a folly.

A deeper wave of colour fused her cheeks as her anger increased. How clever he believed himself to be! He was laughing at her, and she hated him for it. She wanted more than anything to win a victory over him—to show him that he had *not* closed every avenue of escape!—that she would *not* find any great difficulty in taking him unawares.

He looked at her as if expecting some comment, but she had nothing to say, and he too lapsed into silence, assuming a sort of objective detachment, as if he were no longer interested either in her or in the subject about which they had been talking. Sarah's anger subsided, but it was still smouldering beneath the cool exterior she was adopting, and it was with fury as a spur that, immediately after lunch, she determinedly went to look for Yannis in the *perivoli*, where she knew he was pruning the fruit trees.

'*Yassoo!*' she greeted him in his own language, then added in English, 'It is hot for you to be doing this work.'

'Too hot, Madam Carlos.' As if to illustrate just how hot, he drew a handkerchief from his pocket and mopped his brow.

'You would not do this kind of work if you could find some other way of making a living?' Sarah leant with her back against the trunk of a lemon tree and watched him with the pruning shears. The lemon trees always looked so neat and tidy when the more straggly branches had been either shortened or removed altogether. 'I seem to remember you saying you'd like to have a business of your own—a *cafeneion,* I think you said.'

'Yes, that's right.' His eyes brightened momentarily. 'I know of one that is for sale, in the next village to where my people live. One of my sisters wrote to say that it is for sale cheap.' He paused and sighed, then began cutting again.

'How would you like to earn some money, Yannis?' Sarah spoke very softly, watching him turn his head at her words.

'I earn my wages, madam,' he said blankly.

'I meant in addition to your wages.'

Yannis' dark eyes flickered towards her uncertainly.

'Anyone would be happy to make extra money, Madam Carlos,' he said.

A prolonged silence ensued, with Sarah amazed to discover she was fighting the instinct that warned her to hold back, to abandon the idea of enlisting his help. But she must not! Once this chance was lost, she could never envisage another coming her way. She would be here until she had a child; it might be years—or she might never have a child at all.

'I have a proposition to make to you, Yannis,' she said swiftly, in case she should weaken again. 'It's essential that it's kept secret. You understand?'

'Secret, madam?' He was guarded, eyeing her suspiciously.

'I want to get off this island,' she said quickly. 'I need help—your help, Yannis.'

He frowned, his eyes roving her figure before settling on her face.

'You need my help to get off Comaris? But my master's launch—'

'Yannis,' she interrupted, 'I want to leave Mr Carlos—return to my own country.'

He shot her a startled glance and said disbelievingly, 'But you are only married a short time! You are not happy here?'

She bit her lip, hating Carl for this position she was in, having to confide in a servant, bare her soul, tell him everything. No, not everything. There was no need for him to be told very much at all, she realised on giving the matter a little thought. He would be interested only in the reward she was offering. There was no necessity whatsoever for her to confide in him.

'No, Yannis, I am not happy. This country is foreign to me, and I want to go home. Will you help me?'

'But . . . my master—'

'I have something very valuable to give you in return for your help,' she broke in urgently. 'You can sell it, and all your money problems will be solved. Your sisters' dowries can be found, and the little café you want to buy can be yours.'

He looked at her in silence, and she was recalling what she had overheard in the wool shop in the village. Yannis said that Carl only ate and slept with her. He must know, then, that she was not happy.

'The servants think it was strange that our master marry,' he said at last, throwing her an interrogating glance which plainly invited her to explain.

But she merely shook her head. 'That's not relevant.' She frowned. 'Will you help me in exchange for this valuable piece of jewelry I can offer you?'

'I don't know, madam. My master . . .' He gave a small shrug and lapsed into silence. Danger prickles affected Sarah's spine. Supposing she had misread Yannis' character? She did not care to dwell on what particular brand of punishment would be meted out to her if Yannis decided to go to Carl, carrying tales. Should she withdraw—divert the subject and hope that Yannis would forget what she had said? But no. Not only was it too late to draw back, but she had no desire to do so.

'The worst he could do would be to dismiss you from his service, but that would not happen, anyway, because—I presume—you would leave Comaris at the same time as I?' He did not speak, and she added desperately, 'Are you going to help me, Yannis?'

He shrugged. 'How can I, madam?'

'By getting a boat to take me to Rhodes. I did say I had something of great value to offer you,' she said, suddenly guessing that his disinterest was feigned.

'What is this jewel, madam?' he asked, still without any outward sign of enthusiasm.

'I'll show it to you, but not here.' She glanced around. From one window of the house only was this part of the orchard visible—the window of Androula's bedroom. Sarah was taking no chances; she told Yannis she would be in a little arbour beyond the shrubbery. 'You know where I mean,' she added. 'You've seen me there, reading.'

'Yes, madam, I will come along in one . . . two minutes.'

'This is from a grave,' he was saying as he handled

the lovely piece of jewelry a few minutes later. 'I have seen these things in the museum in Athens.' He looked at her suspiciously for several seconds. 'It is stolen, no?'

'I found it, Yannis, so it is mine.'

'Found it, madam? But where?'

'That isn't important,' she answered irritably. 'It's very valuable—*very* valuable. As I've said, you can sell it for a great deal of money.'

He was fingering the rosette thoughtfully, every moment stretching to an hour as Sarah waited, her breathing erratic, for him to come to a decision. At last he nodded and drew a long breath. 'It is a risk, trying to sell this kind of thing—but I have a few contacts . . .' He stopped and nodded his head again. 'I will take it, madam, in exchange for the help you want from me.'

'Thank you . . . thank you very much.'

'You want me to get a boat?'

'Of course. I will have to leave very early in the morning.'

'Your husband . . . Mr Carlos? How can you leave early in the morning?'

'Shall we plan as to my instructions, Yannis?' she suggested, having difficulty with her patience. 'I can be at the harbour at three o'clock . . .' She stopped, gritting her teeth at his surprised expression. 'At three o'clock,' she repeated. 'The night is at its darkest then. Can you get a boat tomorrow morning?'

He shook his head, and she was not surprised. 'The next morning. I have a friend in Rhodes who has a launch. I can telephone him and bring him here for that time you say.'

'Very good—that'll be fine.' She could scarcely speak for the peculiar tightness in her chest. It was painful, the result of excitement and fear and uncertainty, all mingled to blur any intelligent review of her situation. It was enough, though, to hope that Yannis would not let her down. It was all she could do.

Terrified that she would oversleep, Sarah decided not to sleep at all. As soon as Carl had left her she got out of bed and began to dress in slacks and a green cotton sweater. She moved stealthily about the darkened room, afraid to put on a light. She had already done what small amount of packing she intended to do, taking only what she had come with, plus the clothes she was wearing. She still had some money in the form of traveller's cheques, plus a small amount of drachmae picked up in Rhodes when she changed one of her cheques. The money, her passport and the bracelet were in her handbag; she took this, and her one small suitcase, across the room and put them down, and after silently opening the window, she took them onto the verandah. A last look around the room, and a longer, lingering look at the door behind which her husband was sleeping, and she stepped through the window, closing it softly behind her.

She was far too early, and she wished she could have had an hour's sleep. But it was too risky. She would go along to the little arbour and sit there until it was time for her to go to the rendezvous where Yannis would be waiting to accompany her down to the harbour, and then to Rhodes. He had wanted to hand her over to his friend and then return to the villa, having decided not to leave Carl's employ yet.

'I will leave in two . . . three weeks,' he said, 'and then my master will not know it is I who have helped you to get away.'

She refused to agree. For one thing, she was not

happy at the thought of getting on the boat with a strange man, and for another, she had no intention of handing over the bracelet until she had stepped foot on the island of Rhodes and knew she was free.

Yannis was sullen on receiving her reply, and for one panic stricken moment she feared he would change his mind. However, he did agree in the end, saying he would meet her at two o'clock at the small gate which led in one direction to the tomb, and in the other to the harbour.

He was already there when she arrived more than twenty minutes early. She shivered on seeing the dark stocky figure outlined against the shadowed background of a clump of trees. He looked almost grotesque, his back humped by the rucksack it carried. In his hand he had a suitcase, and under his arm a bundle of some kind. How dark it was—and lonely! Yannis whispered something as he took the suitcase; she failed to catch the words, and they started down the hill in silence. No lights from the little clusters of houses nestling in the hills, no lights along the narrow, tree-shaded road. But on the horizon the flickering lights of a ship. No lights in the harbour, but just one lone lantern hanging from above a shop doorway, left on by accident probably.

'It's cold.' Sarah shivered, wanting to cry. She felt so utterly alone in a dark unfriendly world; she had no vision of the future—just a misty void where the making of plans seemed futile.

'The boat will be warm.' Yannis spoke quietly, but she sensed his impatience. He was more than eager to accept the reward, but the actual earning of it was a chore.

They trudged on through the darkness, their footsteps the only sound in a world that seemed to be

dead. And then, suddenly, blindingly, there was a
flare of headlights to accompany the purr of an engine
approaching from behind.

'What!' Yannis spoke, then cursed under his breath.
Sarah could not speak for the great surge of fear that
rose from her heart to her throat, choking her. She
was paralysed, knowing instinctively that it could only
be her husband's car.

Headlights flashed; brakes screeched and the car
slid to a halt beside them. With lightning speed Carl
leapt from the driver's seat, and Sarah gave a little
muffled scream as her arm was crushed in a vise-like
grip. He had a torch; it was flashed into Yannis' face.

'So. . . .' The voice was like that of some jungle
animal enraged to the point of attack. But before he
had time to say another word, Yannis had dropped
Sarah's case and was taking to his heels. Not for
Sarah the safe retreat into the darkness. She felt Carl's
fingers digging into her flesh, saw him wrench the car
door open with a savage gesture. 'Get in!' he ordered,
his voice vibrant with the fury consuming him. Sarah,
her legs ready to collapse beneath her, was thrust
unceremoniously into the car, and the door slammed
upon her. She was trying to think, but her brain was
numbed by fear. Would he murder her . . . ? A
terrified hand stole to her throat, and tears welled up
in her eyes. Carl was beside her, tugging viciously at
the wheel as he swung the car round in the narrow
road. She felt the wheels bump onto the high verge,
then drop off again. Carl jabbed the accelerator; she
was jerked back as the car shot forward at frightening
speed. This, she thought, was more than temper; it
was sheer white-hot fury.

'Carl . . .' She had to speak, to break the terrible
silence that seemed to be closing in on her with every

second that passed, closing relentlessly like a room
that gets smaller and smaller until . . . She felt suffocated, her heart thudding as sledge-hammers worked
overtime inside it. 'Carl . . . I—'

'Save it!' he snarled. 'You'll talk when we get home!'

In no time at all they were at the villa, and Carl
brought the car to a grinding halt on the wide,
semi-circular forecourt. Opening the door with trembling fingers, Sarah managed to get out of the car,
amazed that her shaking limbs would carry her.

'Inside!' Carl's grip was fierce on her arm as he
roughly urged her forward.

'You've no need to worry,' she stammered. 'I'll . . .
n-not try to r-run away.'

'You'd not get far!' She was propelled up the steps.
He opened the door with a key and she was thrust into
the hall, almost losing her balance as she went
staggering forward while Carl closed the door. 'Up-
stairs,' he ordered. 'I warned you that you'd regret it if
you tried to escape, and by God, you *will* regret it!' His
eyes smouldered as Takis suddenly appeared. He said
something to the servant, but Sarah was not interested. She was scarcely able either to walk or to breathe
for the terrible, physical ache of fear possessing her.
She reached the bedroom and went in as Carl flung
wide the door. She heard the click as he closed it and
knew the hopeless despair of being imprisoned for
life.

For a long moment Carl stood there towering over
her, his whole attitude one of merciless domination.

'And now,' he hissed through his teeth, 'you can
explain how you managed to get one of my servants to
help you.'

Sarah heard the venom in his voice, saw the fire in
his black pitchblende eyes, and for a few seconds her

fear was so crushing that her instinct was to apologise, to adopt an air of guilt and contrition, to plead with him for mercy. But even as these thoughts flitted into her brain, something seemed to snap, releasing a deluge of anger which rose to submerge her fear. What right had he to adopt this attitude of dominance?—treating her as if she were one of his down-trodden, subservient Greek women who had been steeped in the tradition of male superiority! What sort of a jelly-fish would she be to cringe before him and beg for mercy! Never! He could kill her first!

'Well,' he rasped, 'I'm waiting.'

'Then you can carry on waiting!' she flashed. 'I don't know if I shall tell you anything.'

'You . . .' He took a step forward, then stopped, obviously taken aback by her unexpected response. 'By God, you will explain! Yannis would never have taken a risk like that unless you'd agreed to pay him well. Where did you get the money?' he demanded, taking another threatening step towards her. 'Where, I say?'

'It's none of your business! I've always warned you that I'd escape if I could, and this business tonight must have convinced you that you *haven't* closed every avenue of escape!' Her own anger was revealed in the eyes that flashed fire at him, her courage in the erect way she was now holding herself, her head lifted high.

'I never reckoned on one of my servants letting me down.' Although his voice still vibrated with the fury possessing him, it seemed less virulent—in fact, Sarah was sure she detected an oppressive note, and guessed that the disloyalty of his servant was upsetting him almost as much as the action of his wife in trying to escape. She had come very close to success;

another twenty minutes and she would have been on board the boat which Carl must have guessed was waiting in the harbour, brought there by Yannis. The sense of failure must be strong within Carl; he was having to admit that he was not infallible, had no fool-proof way of preventing her escape. The very fact that she had managed to enlist the help of one servant made it logical to assume that she could enlist the help of another.

That these—or similar—thoughts were troubling him was proved by his next words, spoken with even less sting in his voice than before. 'What did you bribe him with? He was obviously ready to lose his job here, with me. I know his family needs money for dowries, but you haven't that sort of money to offer—'

'How do you know I haven't?' interrupted Sarah, her indignation stronger than her caution. 'You don't know what I've got.'

'You didn't bring that sort of money out with you from England,' he asserted, shaking his head. 'It would require thousands. . . .' His eyes suddenly lit on her handbag which she had dropped onto the stool in front of the dressing-table, and before she had time to guess at his intention, he had leapt forward to snatch it up. She watched, fascinated and with fear returning, as he took the bag to the bed and turned out the contents. The bracelet was wrapped up in a tissue paper, so it was ignored at first while he examined what was in the purse and then opened up the small leather wallet in which were her traveller's cheques.

'There's nothing much here.' He turned to look at her. 'You'd already paid him?'

She shook her head.

'No . . . I . . . no, I hadn't paid him.'

'Then how . . .?' His eyes returned to the bed and, even more fascinated than before, Sarah watched him unwrap the paper to reveal the bracelet, gleaming in the light, its pristine beauty having been fully restored by the care with which Sarah had cleaned away the dirt from every crevice.

She watched him examining it, saw the wonderment in his eyes and knew that for a few admiring seconds he had forgotten everything except the exquisite object he held in his hand. At last he looked up.

'Where did you get it?' he asked, and now his voice was miraculously free from anger, the aesthetic value of the object having closed his mind to all else.

'From a grave,' she admitted, there being nothing else she could say.

'A grave?'

She nodded. 'I mentioned antiquities, and you said there were temples here. This tomb's on a hillside, and it's Mycenaean.'

She was becoming more and more composed with every minute that passed. It seemed that the bracelet was, for the present anyway, taking Carl's mind completely off the matter of her attempted escape. She realised that she would have to disclose everything about the finding and the working of the site, and supposed that the knowledge of her secrecy would re-arouse his anger, but she did not care. He had got away long enough with domineering over her, and she had come to the end of her endurance. For although she had to admit to being in his power, she had no intention of regarding him as her supreme master.

'How do you know the tomb's Mycenaean?' His dark eyes lifted to hers, puzzlement in their depths.

'I've been digging, along with two young men, Nico

and Panos Palisides.' She stopped as his expression changed. 'You know them, obviously. Well, they were here on vacation from the university.' She went on to tell him everything, from the moment she had suspected the presence of a chamber tomb till the moment when she had gone up there on her own after the departure of the two youths and found the bracelet. 'It proves the grave was robbed,' she added finally.

Carl had listened with the deepest interest all the time, and as she watched him she saw the last of the fire die in his eyes.

'You were doing all that and never said a word to me.' To her amazement he seemed more hurt than angry as he added, 'Why were you so secretive?'

'I wanted to make sure it really was a grave before I asked you to bring in the archaeologists.'

'I see . . .' He paused a moment; and then: 'These two young men—surely they thought it strange that you could spend so much time away from your husband?'

'I told them the truth, Carl—that you spent most of the day in your study.' Sarah was beginning to feel drained and guessed that Carl was affected in the same way. His eyes were brooding as they returned to the object in his hand, and the slight droop of his mouth gave strength to Sarah's suspicion that he was depressed.

'Did they question you about our marriage?'

She shook her head instantly. 'They naturally had a great respect for you. They'd been told of the marriage by their mother, and were surprised, but I expect everyone on the island was surprised.'

He was nodding slowly, turning the bracelet in his hand.

'So this was to be the bribe, I take it?' At last he spoke the words she had been expecting to hear.

'Yes. I offered it to Yannis, and he accepted.'

'You showed it to him?'

'Of course.'

Carl's eyes narrowed as he said, 'This does not belong to you, yet you were going to give it away?' Censure in his voice, which Sarah chose to ignore.

'I was not giving it away,' she denied. 'I was intending to buy my freedom with it.'

A pause, and then: 'And if you had the chance of buying your freedom with another such find?'

'I'd not hesitate. I'm going to get off this island, Carl—I mean it! Don't delude yourself into thinking you can keep me here indefinitely. You know that tonight I was very close to escape. I don't know how you came to find out I'd gone, but if you'd been just a little later, I'd have been on the boat. I'd have escaped—escaped, do you hear?'

'I'd be deaf if I didn't!' There was a glitter of returning anger in his eyes as they settled on her face. 'You didn't escape, though, did you?' he rasped. 'I caught you—'

'Because you were lucky! You might not be so lucky next time!' She was goading him, driven by the bitter disappointment of failure. But she ought to have known better, ought to have practised more caution, because now he was coming towards her, with long purposeful strides that covered the distance between them in seconds. Instinctively she backed away, putting up protective hands in a pathetic little effort to shield herself from attack. His hands shot out to grip her shoulders, and with total loss of control he shook her so violently that his own breathing was laboured when at last he let her go. She was weeping convulsively, sobs shaking her whole body. She put her hands to her shoulders, closing her eyes against the pain inflicted by his merciless fingers. How could she love such a man? How could she have had qualms about leaving him—hesitating because of the pain and humiliation he would suffer? Did he care about the pain *he* inflicted on *her*? On the contrary, he enjoyed it, took a sadistic pleasure in bringing her to tears. When he was holding the bracelet, and his anger had dissolved, she believed she had escaped any punishment for her action in trying to escape, but she ought to have known better, his having warned her over and over again that she would regret any attempt to escape.

'Stop crying!' he ordered. 'You asked for what you got!'

'I c-can't st-stop . . .' A shuddering sob choked the rest and she opened her mouth wide, gasping for air. This natural, primitive gesture born of the need for oxygen had a strange effect on her husband, who stared at her for a moment as if stunned, a nerve pulsating at the side of his neck.

'Sarah . . .' He swallowed something in his throat. 'Sarah . . . don't . . . Don't do that.' His hands this time were gentle as he drew her trembling body into them, guiding her head to his breast and stroking her hair as he murmured over and over again, 'Don't . . . don't cry. Hush, Sarah . . . don't cry.' He tightened his hold, as if by so doing he could control the racking convulsions of her body. 'Oh, God! What makes me . . . ?' He stopped, and when she lifted her eyes she saw that his were closed, as if he had shut them against the pain. 'I came to you and you were gone!' His tone changed, and fury made it harsh.·'Yes, you were gone!' He stopped, and she saw the uncontrollable twist of his mouth, which seemed to reflect an agony raging within him.

'Why did you come?' she asked huskily. 'Why, Carl?' Her heart was throbbing for a different reason now as she waited in a ferment of expectancy, knowing what she wanted and willing him to say the words which she believed to be in his mind.

For she believed he had come to her because he wanted to be with her, to sleep with her, to find comfort in her arms. Yes, surely there could be no other reason why he should come back to her, at that time of the morning.

He looked down into her tear-stained face, and as she saw his expression, her body sagged. For she knew that whatever the reason he had come to her, he had no intention of revealing it.

'It was nothing—nothing important,' he murmured at last. He held her from him, and with a gentle finger brushed a tear from her cheek. Her mouth quivered and he bent to kiss it. 'I don't want to leave you,' he said, surprising her. 'You're so upset.'

'I feel much better, Carl.' What a change, she thought. He was so gentle now, and even contrite. 'I'll be all right, Carl, if you want to go to bed.'

But although he put her from him and turned as if he would leave, he paused and swung around again. 'You wouldn't sleep, would you?'

'You mean *you* wouldn't sleep?' With swift perception she realised that he wanted to stay and talk. He had forgotten all about the escapade; his mind was absorbed by something else. But what? She had once asked him to tell her about his son, and for no reason she could explain, she found herself saying, 'If you won't sleep, Carl, then stay and talk to me. I'd like to hear about your little son.'

'You would? I've been going to tell you about him, Sarah, but the time always seemed to be wrong.'

'It isn't wrong now,' she persisted gently. 'I'll sit down, here on the bed, and you can tell me all about him.'

'You're sure you want me to talk about him?'

'Very sure,' she answered, and sat down.

He began to talk; it was automatic, and he paced the room all the time, never glancing her way. She listened as he told her that, on hearing of her marriage to someone else, he had given up all hope of marrying for love. But he had solemnly promised his great-uncle that he would have a son and heir to inherit the business and fortune when he, Carl, had gone. So he married a Greek woman the same age as himself, married her without bothering to go into her background, as was usual in Greece, the age-old custom being that the families of prospective bride and groom would investigate, making sure, before the marriage, that there was nothing disgraceful on either side. If there was, then the marriage would not take place. Carl had not been interested enough for that. He wanted a son and he was honest with the woman about it. She agreed, and they were married.

'It turned out that she'd been the pillow-friend of several men I knew—business acquaintances,' Carl went on, standing for a moment by the window, staring out towards the sea. 'Whether or not you can understand my feelings, I don't know,' he continued. 'But in Greece a woman is expected to be chaste when she marries. Not only was my wife unchaste, but she was no better than a woman off the streets of Athens.' He paused again, and Sarah noticed his fists clench at his sides—clench so tightly that the knuckles seemed to be coming through the skin. 'By the time I discovered this, she was expecting our child.' He turned then, and Sarah closed her eyes against the evil expression on his face. 'I didn't want the child: if she had died when giving birth I'd have been glad—*glad*, do you hear?'

'Carl,' she pleaded, 'don't work yourself up over it. It's in the past—'

'You can be so calm about it? If you'd married me it would never have happened!'

'I admit it,' she returned huskily. 'But at that time I didn't want to marry anyone—'

'But you did marry! You chose someone else. . . .' His voice faded to silence, and he seemed unable to speak for several seconds. When at length he did, his voice was surprisingly calm and quiet, with that trace of an accent which was always so very attractive to his wife. 'Little Christos was born, and I prayed to God that he would not be like his mother in any way. He was beautiful, Sarah, dark and with black curly hair, and he had strong limbs and a sunny smile. . . .'

Sarah turned away, an ache in her eyes as a cloud of tears built up behind them. This was the Carl she had once known, gentle, idealistic. . . .

'He was a son to be proud of, Sarah, and he was mine. I loved him with all the love I had in me. He was my life, and she was nothing. We lived in separate parts of the house, and although I knew she had pillow-friends, I did not care. But at last I decided to divorce her. She was always jealous of my love for Christos, and when I said I was intending to divorce her, she swore that she would take my little son. I had advice and was told that Christos would be given to me, so I began divorce proceedings.' Even yet again he stopped, and Sarah noticed the beads of perspiration gleaming on his forehead. 'Christos was given to me, but she could have him for one day a month. I did not like that, but the law had said it was to be, and I had to abide by it. Within two months of the divorce she learned she had an incurable disease, and she told someone she had no intention of dying slowly. I only learned of this later. She called for little Christos and took him off in the car. I felt uneasy, but of course I could not stop her from having him. She had planned a terrible revenge. She . . . she . . .' A convulsive shudder shook his whole body, and it seemed that he would be unable to finish the sentence. Sarah, already ahead of him, was crying unashamedly, the tears wet on her lashes. 'She took him and . . . and drove the car over a cliff. Christos died instantly; she lived for two days. . . .'

Sarah closed her eyes tightly, unable to bear the agony that was twisting his face. Her own mind and body seemed to be numbed by the pain he was enduring, living through it all again. He looked at her, but she felt he did not see her. And much as she wanted to go to him, to comfort him with her body, to kiss away the moisture that had gathered in his eyes, she was daunted by the total absence of expression in his gaze. If only there had been a trace of affection, or a silent invitation for her to go to him, she would have gone eagerly. But there was nothing, just a glazed look that told her he was brooding all over again, that his little son was occupying his thoughts to the exclusion of all else.

She sighed, and was suddenly very tired and drained. 'Good night, Carl,' she said softly. 'I think we both need some sleep.'

He nodded, 'Good night, Sarah,' he said briefly, and was gone.

Chapter Twelve

Carl was going to Athens. He had mentioned once or twice that he would have to go, but had never made any firm decision. It had been a matter of puzzlement to Sarah that he could manage to run his business from this remote little island, even though he was in constant touch by telephone with his manager in Athens. She had assumed that the reason why he had not been to the capital was his fear that, in his absence, Sarah might find some way of getting past the strict measures he had taken to keep her on the island. Her recent attempt, which had come so close to success, would, she believed, make him even more reluctant to be away from her. So it came as a surprise when, only a week after her attempt to escape, he announced his intention of going to Athens the following morning.

She just had to say, 'Aren't you afraid I'll escape while you're away?'

'There's no way you can leave Comaris,' he stated, 'unless you can again offer a bribe to one of my servants. But you haven't a bribe large enough, have you?' There was no harshness in his attitude towards her now—not since he had opened his heart to her about his son. In himself he was different, lighter in spirit, as if by talking to Sarah about his child he had lifted some of the burden from his shoulders.

'No, Carl,' she answered quietly, 'I have no bribe large enough now that you have taken the bracelet from me.'

'Nor are you likely to have.' They were at the swimming pool, where for some reason Carl had sought his wife out to tell her what could quite easily have been told later, at the dinner-table. It was not the first time he had sought her out like this; the same thing had happened on the day following her attempted escape, when he had come to her in the little arbour which she so often frequented, always finding in it the peace which she craved. And now, as he sat with her on the pool patio, her mind was a prey to conflicting emotions, for at times like these she could actually glimpse hope for their future together. But it was always a transient hope, because underneath it all, she sensed that he still blamed her for all that had happened to him.

'How long will you be in Athens?' she inquired, breaking into the silence that had fallen upon them.

'Only for a couple of days—tomorrow and Friday. I shall be back about ten o'clock on Friday night.' He paused, regarding her with an odd expression. 'I'd take you with me if it were at all possible,' he said, staggering her.

'You'd . . . enjoy my company?' she asked breathlessly.

'I'd like to show you off to one or two friends of mine. You're very beautiful, Sarah.'

She coloured delicately, and her husband's eyes flickered with interest at what he saw.

'It isn't possible, though, is it, Carl?' she said, and she thought she heard a sigh escape him.

'No, it isn't possible, because you'd run away from me.' His thick lashes were lowered. What was he hiding? She wondered. Pain? Regret? Or a mixture of both?

He went off early, Takis driving him to the harbour, where he boarded his launch. Sarah stood on the terrace and watched the sleek little vessel sail away, and it was inevitable that her thoughts should instantly turn to the possibility of escape. But she could see no way at all, and she began to think she would be a prisoner on Comaris for the rest of her life. She glanced around, able as always to appreciate the beauty—the tapestry of exotic colour in the villa gardens, the timeless fragrance of orange blossom wafting over from the orchard, the slender cypress trees rising like sentinels against the sun-spangled hills. She could have loved this island if she had come to it in different circumstances . . . if she had come to it seven years ago as the bride of a tall, dark, handsome Greek who was madly in love with her. . . .

She turned away as the launch became lost in the shimmering blue haze that lay over the sea, and wondered what she would do with herself. For although the days had always been monotonous, she had at least had Carl's company at meal times, and from dinner time onwards. However, the first day passed more quickly than she had expected; and the next began with a walk along the shore to look at Maroula's villa. It was still shuttered, but the garden was obviously being attended to by the person hired by Carl to look after the villa while its owner was away. However, there were a few weeds growing here and there, and Sarah spent an hour or so pulling them up. After lunch she went up to the site of the tomb and stood for a long while, wondering if the robbers had dropped anything else in their hurry to get away. She

shrugged off the urge to scrape around, telling herself
it would be expecting the impossible to be so lucky a
second time. Not that the bracelet had brought her
any luck, she thought ruefully. Carl had taken it from
her, saying he was sending it to the museum in
Athens. She asked him about bringing in the archaeologists, and he said he would see about it later. As the
grave had been there for three thousand years, it
would not matter if it was left a little while longer.

At last she came away from the site to walk slowly
across the plateau and down to the grounds of the
villa. It was late afternoon, and the sun was descending in a blaze of glory that reflected myriad hues of
orange and gold over the tranquil waters of the
Aegean Sea.

'Mrs Carlos!' she was greeted by Androula as she
entered the house, 'you have a visitor! I have put her
in the lounge, madam, and given her a drink of coffee
and some sandwiches.'

'A visitor, Androula?' Sarah shook her head.
"Who . . .'

'She is your sister.'

'My sister!' Without waiting another second, Sarah
was racing across the hall to enter the lounge, her
chaotic thoughts trying to grapple with what had
happened and how Avril came to be here.

'Sarah!' Avril had been standing by the window,
looking out, waiting impatiently for her sister to put in
an appearance.

'Avril!' A tense, acute silence was the prelude to an
emotional moment such as the sisters had never
experienced before, simply because they had never
been close. But now they both moved at the same
time, as if in answer to a signal, and they were

laughing and crying in each other's arms, Sarah wanting to know how Avril came to be here and Avril babbling something about not expecting Sarah to be looking like this, the picture of health.

'Your letter was so urgent, as if you were being tortured or something. I came without a moment's delay—there'd been enough of that already, and I was in a panic . . .' Avril stopped, drawing away from her sister and giving a deep sigh. 'You're safe, so that's the most important thing.'

'Avril, when did you receive that letter?'

'Only yesterday—believe it or not—and it was delivered by hand. It came inside another letter, addressed to me by a man named Matthew something or other—'

'Yes, he was staying here, and I asked him to post the letter for me. It was months ago!'

'He apologised profusely, said your letter had got into a book he was reading on the plane and he'd forgotten all about it until it fell out the other day. He mentioned something about having a lot of trouble—I think that was the excuse he gave for not posting it. Well, you can imagine my panic! I got on to the airport right away and found I could have a seat on a plane going direct to Rhodes, but I only had about three and a half hours before check-in time. I felt it was no use getting in touch with the Rhodes police after all this time, as I felt that something awful had already happened to you. So I didn't even waste time phoning Eric. I managed to get someone to look after the shop, threw a few things into a bag and took a taxi to the airport. Then, on landing in Rhodes I found there wasn't a regular ferry service to Comaris and I'd have to wait until today. I'd have hired a private launch but was told that Carlos Duris' permission was needed for a launch to land here, so that idea was out, and I had no alternative but to wait for the ferry, which arrived here about half an hour ago. I got a ramshackle old taxi to bring me up from the harbour, and here I am! I've been here about twenty minutes. How was that for speed, seeing that I lost almost a day waiting for the ferry?'

'It's amazing. . . .' Sarah was still a trifle dazed; there was so much to explain and to talk about, but the one stark fact standing out from her tangled thoughts was that she was free. *Free!* She wanted to go outside and shout it so loudly that all the island could hear! Free! It seemed impossible, and she felt she must pinch herself to make sure this was not a dream from which she would awake to find her sister gone, to find she had never been here at all.

But no . . . Avril was very real, and a smile of sheer joy touched Sarah's lips and there was a serenity in her eyes that had been missing since the moment she learned that Eric had left the island without her.

'The Greek girl who showed me in said "her master" was away in Athens.'

'That's right. He comes home tonight—about ten o'clock, he said.'

Avril grimaced but made no comment, saying instead, 'Tell me all about it, Sarah. From your letter it seemed that it couldn't possibly be happening. For Eric to accept a bribe to leave you here . . . I remember Carl, of course, although I never met him. You told me about him being madly in love with you, but it was years ago!'

Sarah nodded, and began to relate exactly what had happened right from the first. It was a lengthy narrative, interspersed with exclamations from Avril—horror, indignation and anger in turn.

'So you're legally married to this Greek?' she said when at last Sarah finished speaking.

'Yes, but I can get a divorce without any trouble once I get home. . . .' Her voice trailed and she did not know why her heart should have lost some of its lightness all at once.

'Of course you can!' agreed Avril through her teeth. 'That man ought to be prosecuted!'

'No, I'd never do that. He's suffered enough already.'

'He deserved to suffer! Who did he think he was, forcing you to have his child?'

'Well, I'm not having his child, for which I'm extremely thankful.'

'But even if you were, you'd not stay with him?'

'Certainly not. I want to go home—back to England and shake the soil of Greece from my feet. . . .' Again her voice trailed, the result of a little pain in the region of her heart.

'You must have had a terrible time,' Avril was saying, compassion mingling with fury in her voice.

Sarah nodded, recalling with a shiver the many occasions when she had suffered the stormy torrent of her husband's anger.

'It was pretty grim, Avril,' she said.

'It's a pity we can't get away before he returns,' said Avril, frowning in thought.

'It's an impossibility for me to get off this island. As I've been telling you, the crew of the ferry are Carl's men, with Takis always there. Carl has given them orders never to let me on board.'

'They must think it very strange, surely?'

'Yes,' agreed Sarah, 'they must. I never let myself dwell on all the talk there must have been over Carl's marriage.'

'Doesn't he care?'

'Not in the least. He's the owner of this island, and as such commands respect, so there isn't any chance of anyone asking him questions. Carl wouldn't care what talk was going on so long as it never came to his ears.'

'We couldn't hire a private launch to take us to Rhodes?' Avril looked questioningly at her sister as she reverted to the subject of getting away. 'You said that this bloke Yannis managed to get one.'

'It wasn't a hired launch. No one could land here, as you yourself found out. It was a boat owned by a friend of Yannis', and Yannis must have known that there'd be no one at the harbour at that time.'

'Oh, well, never mind. You husband will have to let you go, now that I'm here.'

Sarah ordered dinner very early, and the two girls sat a long time over it, each still having a lot of filling in to do. Sarah, commenting on Avril's smart clothes and the way she had done her hair, was told that owning the boutique had changed her whole way of life.

'You have to be smart when you're the proprietress of a shop like that,' she said. 'You'll love it, Sarah. I'll let you have everything at cost. I'm so grateful to you for giving me the money to set myself up. It means such a lot to be independent.'

'You'd never marry again?'

A small pause, and then: 'I admit I've met someone, but I rather think it won't be marriage—too risky! Besides, once bitten, etcetera,' she added with a grimace.

'I'd want marriage or nothing,' murmured Sarah absently, and something in her tone caused Avril to look at her sharply.

'You were always against marriage, because of what happened to Mother and me.'

'I know.'

'You've changed?' queried her sister quietly.

'No . . . er . . . not really.'

'You're still against it?'

'Of course I am.'

'You don't sound too sure.' Her sister was looking at her with an odd expression, and Sarah averted her head, wondering what Avril would say if she were to tell her that she had fallen in love with the man who had kept her prisoner. 'Have you left anything out, Sarah?' Avril's question was so unexpected that Sarah gave a start.

'What do you mean?'

Avril was silent for a space, considering. 'I hadn't noticed it before, because we were both talking, having so much to say to one another, but now . . . well, I feel instinctively that you're keeping something back.'

Sarah shrugged, feigning surprise. 'What could I be keeping back? I haven't gone into the intimate part of our life together, but—'

'I didn't expect you to; it must have been purgatory anyway. No, it wasn't that.' She stopped, an inquiring expression on her face, but Sarah remained silent, thinking about the word 'purgatory' and speculating on her sister's reaction were she to tell her that the word 'heaven' would have been far more apt. 'It's something else, Sarah,' Avril went on presently. 'You've a secret, haven't you?'

A sigh, and then: 'It's not important, Avril. The

important thing is that I'm free, that Carl no longer has any power to keep me here.'

'No, indeed. I only wish that bloke Matthew had posted your letter when he should have done. You'd have been away from here a long while ago.'

'A long while ago. . . .' Sarah spoke to herself. 'When my heart was free. . . .' She averted her head again to hide her expression and said, changing the subject, 'I wonder what my flat'll be like? Everything will be covered with dust, and moths will have got into the carpets.' A depression was coming over her, and she determinedly shook if off. Freedom! She repeated the word over and over again in her mind. Freedom was hers! She had nothing to be depressed about, nothing at all.

'I reckon you should make Eric pay for anything that's ruined,' advised Avril. 'He'll be glad to pay if you threaten him with prosecution.'

'I'm not having anything at all to do with him. At first I thought I would—I felt I'd go along to the office and let him have the length of my tongue, but now I just want to forget everything and begin all over again.'

They finished the excellent meal, took coffee and liqueurs in the lounge and then sat out on the terrace, enjoying the cool breeze and the heady perfumes it gathered as it drifted over the garden.

'I must admit,' said Avril, 'that this place is idyllic. Carl must be a very wealthy man.'

'He inherited a lot of money from his uncle, plus the business and this house.'

'You ought to sue him for maintenance.'

'No, I'm not doing anything like that.' She glanced at her watch by the light of a lantern in the vines above her head. 'A quarter past nine. . . .' She had not realised it was so late, the time having flown since the arrival of her sister. 'Carl will be here soon.'

Avril made a face. 'I can't say I'm looking forward to meeting him. What a shock he's going to get when he finds me here. He'll gnash his teeth at the idea that he didn't guess you'd have written a letter and given it to Matthew to post.'

Sarah nodded absently, trying to shake off the dampening effect of Avril's words. 'Yes, he'll certainly receive a shock.'

'He must be a very strange man,' mused Avril, 'to sit in his study all day long. Doesn't he ever want any recreation?'

Sarah shook her head; it was not a negative gesture but an attempt to dispel the picture which her mind was conjuring up: the shock which Avril had mentioned, then the ensuing sense of total defeat as Carl was forced to accept that his power over his wife was at an end. The humiliation when everyone on the island learned that she had left him, the gossip of the servants who had already guessed that something was very wrong with the marriage. Carl alone in his misery . . . alone in that room all day, with not even company for meals. . . .

Sarah caught her underlip between her teeth, bending her head as she noticed Avril's intent stare fixed upon her. 'Carl's a very unhappy man,' she quavered, choking back the tears in her voice. 'No, he has no recreation. He has . . . nothing, nothing at all to brighten his life.'

'Does he deserve anything to brighten it?'

'It was so tragic about his son.'

'He's not the first man to lose a son.'

'The Greeks adore children. In any case, little Christos was all he had.' She was unconscious of the fact that her eyes were shadowed with pain, but acutely conscious of the rush of tenderness invading her heart.

'You're sorry for him, aren't you?' Avril stared at her through wide, disbelieving eyes. 'You always were a little softie, Sarah. That's why you married that beast Arthur Grimsby. All you could think of at the time was Mother, not yourself.' She paused in thought as something occurred to her. 'If I'd been in your position, I'd have told Carl why I married. I couldn't have let him go on blaming me when I was innocent.'

'It would have made no difference,' returned Sarah flatly. 'He was always ready to condemn me. He hates me, I've told you that—hates me for turning him down in the first place.'

'From what I've gathered, he hates you for marrying someone else when you'd stated, so emphatically, that you were against marriage.' Sarah said nothing, and Avril went on, as if she just had to, 'For someone to be against marriage and then be forced into it, not once, but twice! It seems too fantastic to be true.'

Sarah nodded mechanically. She glanced at her watch again, and was seized with a nerve-twisting tension. 'I wonder if he'll be on time?' she murmured almost to herself. 'He said ten, but he could be later. . . .'

'Or a little earlier. I expect this is his car coming up the drive.'

Sarah, who heard the purr of the engine as her sister spoke, twisted her head, her heart pounding against her ribs. But how absurd to be afraid! Avril was with her; the next few minutes might be uncomfortable for them all, but they would soon be over.

The car crunched along the gravel, then stopped.

The headlights were reduced in brilliance and Carl's figure was dark as it passed in front of them.

'Let's go inside,' suggested Sarah, trying to be calm. 'We can't talk out here.'

'You're as white as a sheet,' observed Avril a few minutes later when they were in the lounge.

'I feel it,' Sarah admitted. 'I wish this next five or ten minutes were over.'

'Will he come in here?' asked Avril, listening.

'He might go to his study.'

'Call him, then, as he passes the door.'

Sarah opened her mouth, then closed it again, unable to speak for the constriction in her throat. She was aware of Carl's footsteps in the hall, then of Avril swiftly crossing the room to open the door. She felt a rush of panic, an urge to flee . . . but her legs would not have obliged anyway.

'Mr Duris—will you come into the lounge?' Avril's voice, quiet but imperious. Sarah wished she could borrow some of her self-confidence.

'Who the . . . ?' Carl was at the door, staring from the threshold, and in the few seconds while he stood, uncomprehending, Sarah gasped at the fleeting impression of a difference in his appearance. Erased were the harsh lines of his face, the grim and drawn expression, and in their place . . . hope? Expectancy? 'Who the devil are you?' he demanded, recovering instantly and striding into the room. Sarah could only stare at him, unwilling to admit that the change had been an illusion, and yet here he was, just the same as usual: the harsh lines were there, the pagan eyes. . . .

'This is my sister, Avril,' she heard herself say. 'Avril . . . my husband.' She spoke jerkily, continuing before either could acknowledge the introductions, 'I

sent Avril a letter by Matthew. It was delayed—he
forgot to post it—but Avril received it in the end. And
she came immediately.'

'Your sister. . . .' His clenched hands were the only
sign of emotion, but he seemed to shrink, as if losing
some of his impressive stature. 'You wrote to her—
sending the letter by Maroula's nephew?'

'Yes, Carl, that's right.' Where, Sarah wondered,
was the fury she had steeled herself for?

'I asked you if you'd enlisted his help.'

'I didn't try to get help directly,' she explained. 'I
merely gave him a letter to post.'

'And all this time . . .' He glanced away from her to
look at Avril, then returned his gaze to Sarah. 'All this
time you were waiting, wondering what had happened to your letter?'

Sarah could only nod her head, for her throat still
felt blocked, so that even swallowing was difficult.

'This Matthew,' intervened Avril, 'had mislaid the
letter and found it only the other day.'

'I see. . . .' His eyes were suddenly lifeless; he
seemed totally drained of all ability to feel. 'When do
you want to leave?' he asked his wife, and both she
and Avril gasped at this instant acceptance of defeat.
Where, Sarah asked herself, was the satisfaction she
should be feeling? Suddenly she knew a surge of
bitter disappointment, a great wave of emotion that
threatened to suffocate her.

Deep in her subconscious she had been hoping,
praying, that Carl would ask her to stay, and whether
he had pleaded or commanded, it would not have
mattered. All she had desired was to learn that he
wanted her to stay.

Tears filled her eyes, but she was too proud to let

him see them fall. He had regretted his action in bringing her here, regretted it because a child was not on the way. He had probably become convinced that she never would have a child, and so he was not sorry to see her go.

As from a great distance she heard Avril say, 'We'd like to go as soon as possible, but the ferry—'

'I'll arrange for my launch to take you to Rhodes first thing in the morning,' and without another glance at his wife, he swung on his heel and was gone.

The morning was grey, suiting Sarah's mood as she sat next to Avril in the car, looking blindly at the back of Takis' head. How ironic that she had come to Comaris reluctantly and she was leaving even more reluctantly. If only Carl had wanted her for some reason other than to give him a child . . .

He had not even been there to say good-bye; she had looked for him in his bedroom and study and had even gone along the shore to see if he was walking there. Deliberately he had kept out of her way.

'You're very quiet, Sarah.' Avril's voice broke into her train of thought, and she managed to produce a thin smile.

'It's strange to be leaving, Avril.'

'Don't tell me you've any regrets?'

Sarah was silent. They were approaching the harbour, and there, waiting, was her husband's launch, the same that had brought her and Eric over . . . so very long ago, it seemed, and it *looked* just the same, she was thinking later as she stood by the rail, chaotic thoughts coalescing as she tried in vain to separate her love from her compassion, Carl's hatred from his pride. . . .

Pride . . . Could it have been his sensitive, uncompromising pride that had prevented him from asking her to stay? When he had been in a position to force her to stay, that had been different, but if he wanted her now, he would have to ask. . . .

Her pulses began to throb in unison with the engines, and at the same time some compulsion drew her eyes upwards, and she saw the lone bowed figure of her husband on the terrace. Her heart twisted, almost wrenched from its moorings in an agony of pain. She closed her eyes, conscious of tears trapped beneath the lids. Tears of pity? It was not pity that made her call to Takis, telling him she wanted to get off the boat.

'What!' Avril swung round from the rail. 'You've forgotten something?'

'I'm going back,' she stated huskily. 'My . . . my place is with my husband.'

Avril could only stare, shaking her head. 'Are you crazy?' she said at last.

'Possibly,' Sarah owned with a curious indrawn breath that was almost a sob, 'because I'm not sure whether he wants me or not.' How would he receive her? Would he send her away again?

'Mrs Carlos, did you call?'

'Yes, Takis. I'm getting off the boat. I want you to drive me back to the villa.'

He stared; then his thick dark lashes came down. The servants would have something else to gossip about, thought Sarah absently.

'I will take you back, then—'

'Sarah,' interrupted Avril urgently, 'you can't be such a fool! It's pity, isn't it? I knew last night. I told you you're a little softie, putting others before yourself

All right—it's a shame for him, but that's no reason why you should sacrifice yourself. . . .' Her voice trailed to silence as Sarah flicked a hand, reminding Avril that Takis was standing there, listening.

'I go to the car,' said Takis obligingly, 'and wait for you.'

He went away; she heard him talking to Petros, then saw him getting off the boat, carrying her suitcase.

'Let's sit down,' suggested Avril, 'and talk this over.'

But Sarah was shaking her head, her eyes raised to the dark outline of her husband's figure.

'I'm going back.'

'It doesn't make sense,' exploded Avril. 'You wrote that letter, telling me you were a prisoner and begging me to help you escape, and now you want to go back to the prison! You must be out of your mind!'

Sarah looked at her, tears filming her eyes. 'I love him,' she said simply and turned away, too full to say more.

'You . . . love him? A man like that?' Avril's voice, incredulous and faintly scornful, was yet strangely understanding, and Sarah was reminded that it had taken her sister a long, long time to get over her love for her husband. 'What fools women are,' added Avril, enraged, 'products of a capricious nature that made us so damned soft and men so hard!'

'Carl isn't hard,' murmured Sarah in defence of him.

'Well, you should know,' retorted Avril significantly.

'He was kind and gentle once, and . . . and madly in love with me.'

'But he isn't in love with you now, because if he was, he wouldn't have let you go without putting up some sort of a fight. It seemed to me that he was quite happy at the idea of your leaving him.'

Sarah merely nodded, agreeing silently while at the same time thinking again that it might have been his pride that silenced his tongue.

'Takis is waiting,' she said, flicking a hand automatically towards the car, which was now standing opposite to where the launch, its engines now silent, was moored. 'I'm sorry, Avril, for all the trouble I've caused . . ' She stopped and turned to her, deep affection and gratitude in her eyes. 'It wasn't wasted, though, because it was only when escape was absolutely certain that I realised I didn't want it.'

'Thanks,' sarcastically, from Avril, and then: 'your mind's firmly made up?'

'Yes, Avril, it is.'

'Then there's nothing I can do.' She paused a moment. 'I can't come back with you, Sarah, because the woman I've entrusted the shop to can't stay more than four days. She's going off to Spain on Saturday.'

'It's all right. But you'll come for a holiday sometime?'

'I might,' was Avril's stiff, impatient rejoinder.

'I'm sorry,' began Sarah again, but Avril interrupted her.

'Don't apologise any more, Sarah. I only hope it turns out right—but it seems impossible that it can.'

'I'll come over to see you,' promised Sarah, bypassing her remark. 'Carl used to go to London frequently on business, and if he starts again, I'll come with him.'

'We'll write in any case,' declared Avril firmly. 'We must keep in closer touch than before: I want to know how you're getting on.' A pause, but Sarah had nothing to say. 'I want to thank you again for that money,' Avril said presently. 'I'll never forget, and if there's anything I can do, then don't waste any time. Just let me know.'

'Thank you,' returned Sarah. 'I know you feel convinced I'm making a mistake, but I must go back . . . I must.'

'Good luck, then,' was all Avril said, and presently they were saying good-bye.

'I'll tell Takis to come straight back,' promised Sarah, 'to help Petros with the boat. You'll be in Rhodes by half-past ten.'

Ten minutes later the car was pulling up at the front of the villa. Carl was standing there on the white marble steps, and it struck Sarah that from his vantage point on the terrace he would have seen her leave the launch and get into the car. She got out of the car unsteadily, because her legs seemed to have lost their strength; vaguely she was aware of Takis taking her case from the boot and putting it down instead of taking it into the hall, which would have necessitated his passing Carl. He was being very tactful, she realised, for he was in the car and driving away within seconds of drawing up.

For a long tense, profound moment Carl and Sarah stood there, each with questioning eyes.

Carl was the first to speak, the huskiness in his voice betraying the depth of his emotions. 'You've come back to . . . to me?' His eyes slid from her white face to the suitcase standing there, occupying a tiny space on the wide forecourt, not far from where she stood. 'It's true—you've come to stay?'

She nodded, taking an unsteady step forward.

'If you want me to stay, Carl, then . . . yes, I've come to stay. . . .' Her voice trailed to silence. He was coming down the steps towards her, his arms outstretched. He took both her hands in his, staring down at them for a moment before bringing them to his lips. He was unable to speak, but what Sarah encountered in his eyes brought forth a little gasp of disbelief.

'Carl,' she stammered, 'Y-you . . . you love me?' Even as she spoke she would have taken back the words, for suddenly she doubted what she had seen in his eyes. But there could be no doubting the gentleness of his hands as they slid to her waist; and at the tender love in his kiss, her eyes brimmed with tears. He looked down into her lovely face, and his smile sent her heart racing, her spirits soaring to the clouds. It was a profound moment of emotion for them both, with many questions to be asked and answered; yet none were of any importance in the supreme joy that had come to them so unexpectedly.

He drew his lips away, to look deeply into her eyes. 'My Sarah, I have so much to say to you, dear.' His arm slid about her shoulder, and silently they went into the house, and into the lounge, where there was no danger of being seen by the servants. 'But first, dearest, tell me what happened—why you decided to come back.' His hands were at her waist again, almost spanning it, and she quivered as she felt their tender warmth through the thin material of her dress.

'I came back because I love you,' she answered simply.

'But this morning—you must have been very sure you wanted to leave me?' Half a statement and half a question.

Sarah shook her head. 'I wasn't sure, Carl, but I felt it was for the best. But just now—on the boat—I knew I couldn't go. Even if you didn't love me, I'd have to stay with you.'

'You'd have known I love you last night if you'd been alone when I returned from Athens.'

'I would?' She was recalling her impression, the fleeting glimpse of a change in his appearance. 'Why . . . what . . . ?'

'I ran into your old employer; he was in Athens, buying property. We were in the same hotel and met in the lounge-bar. He had had too much to drink and was talkative as a result. I learned why you had married, and also that you'd come into a fortune. I gathered that Vernon had asked you to marry him after he got into difficulties. He was resentful that you were giving the money to charity, and he also seemed resentful because he was sure you had given your sister money to go into business.' He stopped, but Sarah said nothing, merely nodding automatically as a gesture of agreement to what he had said. 'I was furious with you for allowing me to misjudge you,' continued Carl presently, 'but then I was admitting it was all my own fault. I'd given you no encouragement to confide—'

'I almost did, all the same,' she interrupted, 'and I wish now I had done. But I suppose obstinacy was one thing that held me back—and the conviction that you could never love me anyway.'

Silence enfolded them for a long moment while he held her to his heart, kissing her tenderly.

'I'm beginning to think that I never stopped loving you,' he confessed. 'Why didn't I admit it instead of hurting you, making you pay for all the empty years, and the loss of my son? When I'd been kind to you, I despised myself, because I believed the worst of you.' He paused and frowned, and Sarah now knew the reason for his changing moods. 'That night when you tried to escape,' he went on, still frowning, 'I couldn't fight it any longer and came to you to tell you I loved you, that we'd forget the past and begin again—if you wanted me, that was.'

'Oh. . . .' She drew away, an ache catching her throat. 'Do you know, Carl, I did wonder if that was the reason why you came. And it was only to find me gone. . . .' She broke off with a choking little sound and within seconds she was in his arms, as she had been in his arms so many times before, but this was different. He loved her. . . .

'Carl,' she managed breathlessly when he had stopped kissing her, 'last night, when you returned, you looked so different—'

'Because I'd been talking to Vernon. I intended telling you I loved you . . .' He broke off, his black brows contracting in a frown. 'I ought not to have let you go, darling, but it did something to me, seeing your sister there. I knew a terrible feeling of defeat.'

'If only I'd known,' she said, and started to cry.

Carl held her from him, a trifle dazed. 'Darling, what on earth is there to cry about?'

'It's j-just th-that we nearly l-lost each other!'

'I'm beginning to believe there never was any danger of our losing one another, my darling.'

'If only I'd married you seven years ago,' she quavered. 'None of your suffering would ever have happened—' She stopped as Carl's hand touched her mouth.

'The past is gone,' he said. 'It's the future we're facing, dearest, our future.'

Lifting her head, she looked at him through her tears. 'You really mean that, Carl?'

'I really mean it.' His response was firm. 'I've

finished dwelling in the past, because the future holds so much for me now that I have you.'

She snuggled close, deliberately crushing her breasts against the hardness of his chest. He bent to kiss her and warned, 'Careful, darling. I'm not made of ice, as you very well know.'

She laughed shakily and snuggled closer, lifting her fact in a subtle invitation for him to possess her lips. He smiled in some amusement, and she coloured at his perception.

'So you're asking for it, are you?' He bent his head, and she thrilled to his fierce, demanding mouth, quivered at the contact of his hand as it slid over her breast. Inevitably the movement of her slender, seductive body was fuel to the flame of his passion, and Sarah found herself swept irresistibly into the vortex of his passion, pleasure and pain mingling in a thrill of ecstasy that ripped through her body, leaving her limp in his arms. supported by his strength. He looked down with all the old familiar triumph in his eyes, but now there was love and tenderness, too, and the kind of adoration which Sarah had known a long while ago.

'My darling,' she whispered huskily. 'My own darling husband. . . . Oh, why should I be so lucky!'

'I'm the lucky one, my dearest. I don't know how you could love me, when I'd treated you so abominably.'

She had tried to stop him, and when she failed, she only laughed at what he had said. It was as nothing, now that it, too, was in the past.

For a long while they were quiet, lost in dreams of the future, but eventually Sarah said, looking up at him, 'Carl, shall we be going to London? You see, I want to visit Avril—'

'Avril! Good Lord, I'd forgotten her! Where is she?'

'She had to go, but I promised we'd go and visit her. Can we, Carl?'

'Of course, sweetheart. Wherever I go, you shall go with me.' At his tender expression her eyes glowed with joy. She tried to speak but was too full to say what was in her heart, and so she merely gave a quivering sigh and lifted her face, inviting his kiss.

Silhouette Romance

IT'S YOUR OWN SPECIAL TIME

Contemporary romances for today's women.
Each month, six very special love stories will be yours
from SILHOUETTE. Look for them wherever books are sold
or order now from the coupon below.

$1.50 each

___ #61	WHISPER MY NAME Michaels	___ #80	WONDER AND WILD DESIRE Stephens
___ #62	STAND-IN BRIDE Halston	___ #81	IRISH THOROUGHBRED Roberts
___ #63	SNOWFLAKES IN THE SUN Brent	___ #82	THE HOSTAGE BRIDE Dailey
___ #64	SHADOW OF APOLLO Hampson	___ #83	LOVE LEGACY Halston
___ #65	A TOUCH OF MAGIC Hunter	___ #84	VEIL OF GOLD Vitek
___ #66	PROMISES FROM THE PAST Vitek	___ #85	OUTBACK SUMMER John
___ #67	ISLAND CONQUEST Hastings	___ #86	THE MOTH AND THE FLAME Adams
___ #68	THE MARRIAGE BARGAIN Scott	___ #87	BEYOND TOMORROW Michaels
___ #69	WEST OF THE MOON St. George	___ #88	AND THEN CAME DAWN Stanford
___ #70	MADE FOR EACH OTHER Afton Bonds	___ #89	A PASSIONATE BUSINESS James
___ #71	A SECOND CHANCE ON LOVE Ripy	___ #90	WILD LADY Major
___ #72	ANGRY LOVER Beckman	___ #91	WRITTEN IN THE STARS Hunter
___ #73	WREN OF PARADISE Browning	___ #92	DESERT DEVIL McKay
___ #74	WINTER DREAMS Trent	___ #93	EAST OF TODAY Browning
___ #75	DIVIDE THE WIND Carroll	___ #94	ENCHANTMENT Hampson
___ #76	BURNING MEMORIES Hardy	___ #95	FOURTEEN KARAT BEAUTY Wisdom
___ #77	SECRET MARRIAGE Cork	___ #96	LOVE'S TREACHEROUS JOURNEY Beckma
___ #78	DOUBLE OR NOTHING Oliver	___ #97	WANDERER'S DREAM Clay
___ #79	TO START AGAIN Halldorson	___ #98	MIDNIGHT WINE St. George
		___ #99	TO HAVE, TO HOLD Camp

$1.75 each

___ # 100	YESTERDAY'S SHADOW Stanford	___ # 112	WHISPER WIND Stanford
___ # 101	PLAYING WITH FIRE Hardy	___ # 113	WINTER BLOSSOM Browning
___ # 102	WINNER TAKE ALL Hastings	___ # 114	PAINT ME RAINBOWS Michaels
___ # 103	BY HONOUR BOUND Cork	___ # 115	A MAN FOR ALWAYS John
___ # 104	WHERE THE HEART IS Vitek	___ # 116	AGAINST THE WIND Lindley
___ # 105	MISTAKEN IDENTITY Eden	___ # 117	MANHATTAN MASQUERADE Scott
___ # 106	THE LANCASTER MEN Dailey	___ # 118	FOR THE LOVE OF GOD Dailey
___ # 107	TEARS OF MORNING Bright	___ # 119	DESIRE Hampson
___ # 108	FASCINATION Hampson	___ # 120	TAKE THIS LOVE Carroll
___ # 109	FIRE UNDER SNOW Vernon	___ # 121	JUST LIKE YESTERDAY Langan
___ # 110	A STRANGER'S WIFE Trent	___ # 122	WINTERFIRE Scofield
___ # 111	WAYWARD LOVER South	___ # 123	HOLIDAY IN JAMAICA Sinclair

---

SILHOUETTE BOOKS. Department SB/1
1230 Avenue of the Americas
New York, NY 10020

Please send me the books I have checked above. I am enclosing
$_____ (please add 50¢ to cover postage and handling. NYS and
NYC residents please add appropriate sales tax). Send check or
money order—no cash or C.O.D.'s please. Allow six weeks for delivery.

NAME_____

ADDRESS_____

CITY_____ STATE/ZIP_____

READERS' COMMENTS ON SILHOUETTE ROMANCES:

"Your books are written with so much feeling and quality that they make you feel as if you are part of the story."

—D.C.*, Piedmont, SC

"I'm very particular about the types of romances I read; yours more than fill my thirst for reading."

—C.D., Oxford, MI

"I hope Silhouette novels stay around for many years to come. . . . Keep up the good work."

—P.C., Frederick, MD

"What a relief to be able to escape in a well-written romantic story."

—E.N.. Santa Maria, CA

"Silhouette Romances . . . Fantastic!"

—M.D., Bell, CA

"I'm pleased to be adding your books to my collection—my library is growing in size every day."

—B.L., La Crescenta, CA

* Names available on request.